The Chemistry Of
WHEAT STARCH AND GLUTEN
And Their Conversion Products

THE CHEMISTRY OF

WHEAT STARCH

AND

GLUTEN

AND THEIR CONVERSION PRODUCTS

J. W. KNIGHT

B.Sc., Ph.D.(Lond.), F.R.I.C., F.R.A.C.I.
Formerly Technical Director, Geo. Fielder Group,
Tamworth, Australia

LEONARD HILL : LONDON

1965

A Leonard Hill Book
First published in Great Britain 1965 by
The Book Division
Grampian Press Limited
St. Richard's House
94–96 Eversholt Street
London, N.W.1

Printed in Great Britain
by Butler & Tanner Ltd., Frome and London

Bound by
Mansell (Bookbinders) Ltd., London

PREFACE

THROUGHOUT the world the production of starch comprises a major industry, and in one or other of its many forms starch finds its way into most of the facets of our modern way of living. Indeed, it has been said that the level of usage of starch products by a nation indicates the level of the standard of living in that nation.

The production of protein is likewise of great importance, and many of the undeveloped countries of the world are badly in need of more protein in their food, while in the United States of America and in Europe slimming foods are big business.

In Australia, both starch and protein are produced by the extraction of wheat flour. This process is the major source of the Commonwealth's starch supply, and Australian gluten is known and used throughout the world.

This little book has been written mainly as a result of personal experience within the Australian starch and gluten industry and is by no means a comprehensive study. It is hoped, however, that it will prove to be of interest to scientific and technical workers in the starch, gluten and food fields in many countries. The writing has an emphasis on the practical side of the subjects.

I wish to thank Messrs. G. K. Adkins and E. G. Woodward, both of Wheat Industries Pty, Tamworth, Australia, for their help. My thanks are due also to Messrs. Reckitt & Sons Ltd, Hull, England, for permission to publish results obtained in their research laboratories. I am indebted to the Geo. Fielder Group of Australia for permission to take photographs in their factory at Tamworth and to publish them in this book.

J. W. KNIGHT

Tamworth, N.S.W.,
  Australia.

Present address:
c/o Corn Products Ltd,
Trafford Park,
Manchester 17,
England.

CONTENTS

LIST OF PLATES

LIST OF FIGURES

xi

MANUFACTURE OF STARCH AND GLUTEN FROM FLOUR

INTRODUCTION

THE raw material for the preparation of wheat starch and gluten is the wheat grain, and it is proper here to give a number of brief details about the growing of wheat.

Wheat is a grass of the Gramineae family and of the genus *Triticum*, and was probably the first cereal crop to be grown by man. This is thought to be during the Neolithic period some 6,000 to 7,000 years ago. Today, throughout the world, some 450 million acres are under cultivation for the growing of wheat. Although it can grow in vastly different climates and different soils, wheat grows best in the temperate, drier regions of the world with a latitude between 30° and 60° and having a rainfall of between 12 in. and 36 in. per year. The prairies of the North American continent and of the U.S.S.R. are good examples of the correct conditions.

The yield of wheat grain per acre varies widely from area to area and within the same area from season to season. Under dry conditions in some parts of the world the yield is as low as 10 bushels per acre, whilst 80 bushels per acre have been recorded in some parts of Europe. In paddocks which are irrigated much higher yields have been reported, but this measure is rarely employed.

Work is being carried out continuously by plant breeders to produce different varieties of wheat. Some of the first selection of varieties was begun in France as early as 1850, whilst William Farrer in Australia began a planned breeding programme in 1880. While, however, most of the early work was based on a selection from the variations present in the commonly grown wheats, this does not create new genetic combinations, and present-day plant breeders have entirely resorted to the crossing of different varieties. The main objectives in wheat breeding are disease resistance, stronger straw, insect resistance, wheats for specific uses, heat and cold resistance and, of course, higher yielding wheats.

The wheat grain can be divided roughly into three parts in the following proportions:

(*a*) Germ 2% ; (*b*) Endosperm 85% ; (*c*) Husk 13%

The germ is especially valued because of its high protein and fat content, and the husk contains no worthwhile quantity of starch. Thus it is the endosperm that is of prime importance in starch manufacture. Since present-day milling techniques aim at effecting a clean separation of endosperm from the outer husks and germ, flour is the obvious choice for the starch and gluten process.

The wheat endosperm has a cellular structure, and each cell, contained within thin cellulose walls, is filled with starch granules varying in diameter size from 1 to 40 μ. Between these starch granules the space is filled with a proteinaceous material which contains, besides the proteins, much of the mineral matter, colouring matter and enzyme content of the endosperm. In the mind's eye it can be thought of as very similar to nut toffee made with irregular-sized nuts.

When the endosperm is milled into flour the cells break up and form endosperm agglomerates, free starch granules, broken starch and a broken proteinaceous matrix. Thus it is that flour contains free starch, and if this fraction were large enough one could speculate on various dry processes to separate the starch in a pure state. This ideal state of affairs would eliminate much of the starch manufacturers' headaches and would also result in a high protein fraction of flour in which the protein would be in its natural state, and not somewhat denatured, as happens in the conventional gluten/starch process.

In recent years an air-classification process has been developed which, however, only goes partly along the road to this goal. The

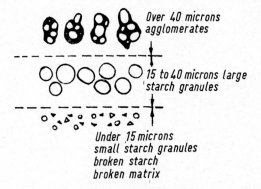

FIG. 1. Feed to an air classifier.

flour is specially ground in an impact grinder which considerably reduces the particle size without greatly increasing the damaged starch content. The size distribution of the components will vary according to whether the flour is soft or hard, but as an example and taking a soft wheat, the endosperm agglomerates are over 40 μ, the free starch granules 15 to 40 μ and the small starch granules, broken starch and broken protein matrix are under 15 μ in diameter. The special grinding reduces the proportion of over 40-μ-sized particles to the smaller fractions without breaking up the individual starch granules. This fine flour is now treated in an air centrifugal separator in which large air-drag forces are counterbalanced by strong centrifugal forces to give the required cut points at reasonable air and stock capacity (Fig. 1).

Typical results are shown:

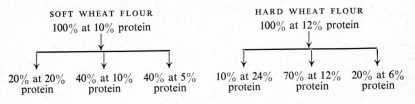

SOFT WHEAT FLOUR
100% at 10% protein

HARD WHEAT FLOUR
100% at 12% protein

20% at 20% protein   40% at 10% protein   40% at 5% protein   10% at 24% protein   70% at 12% protein   20% at 6% protein

TRADITIONAL METHODS

When flour is mixed with water in the right proportion a dough is formed. Wheat protein has the property of hydrating to form wet gluten, a typically ductile, tenacious and elastic mass, and it is this property that makes possible the formation of dough from flour.

Among the oldest and best-tried methods for the preparation of starch and gluten is the so-called Martin process, in which dry milled wheat is formed into a dough with about 60% of its weight of water. By suitable methods the starch is washed away from the gluten, which is retained as a single coherent mass. This process is specifically designed to prevent the gluten breaking into small pieces and passing into the starch slurry.

A practical experiment can illustrate the point. If a small quantity of dough is made and left to mature for 30 minutes, this can then be taken and gently squeezed in the hand beneath a slow stream of water from a cold water tap. By gently manipulating the dough, the starch is separated in a milky slurry and the gluten is retained in the hand as a single coherent mass.

The Martin process, with some variations, has been successfully used throughout the years, and it can be made to give good products in good yields. This very important process, operating continuously under modern conditions, will now be described in some detail.

Stage 1 in Detail

Flour. The type of flour used as the starting material for this process must be carefully controlled, since the different types vary considerably in their behaviour when made up into doughs. Hard flours contain a relatively high content of protein with strong elastic gluten, while soft flours produce a gluten that is less elastic and which is easily torn apart and crumbled. A high-protein Manitoba flour is a

STAGE 1

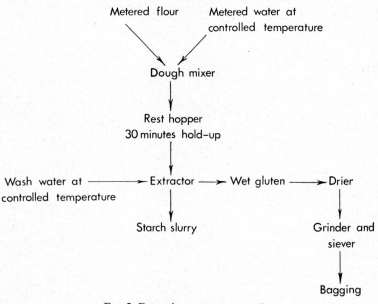

Fig. 2. Extraction process—stage 1.

good type to use, while an English soft-type flour produces a starch slurry that is seriously contaminated with protein and which is more difficult to purify.

If a soft flour must be used for this process, then the addition of a small proportion of an inorganic salt, and in particular sodium chloride, will toughen up the gluten. This is a well-known trick among operators in the industry to try to improve matters when break-up of the gluten is encountered.

A regular laboratory examination of the flour is necessary, and it is also very desirable that at the same time a sample be actually made up into a dough and washed out. In this way a practical determina-

STAGE 2

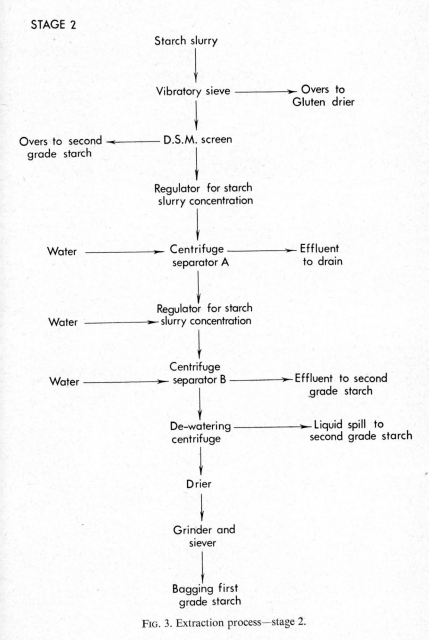

FIG. 3. Extraction process—stage 2.

tion of the yields to be expected and the behaviour of the gluten can be made. Provided the conditions for this determination are kept strictly constant, the results will be comparable, although not necessarily in strict agreement, with the yields obtained in production.

In a more fundamental manner, the flour should be examined for protein content, soluble matter, moisture and starch. The total

STAGE 3

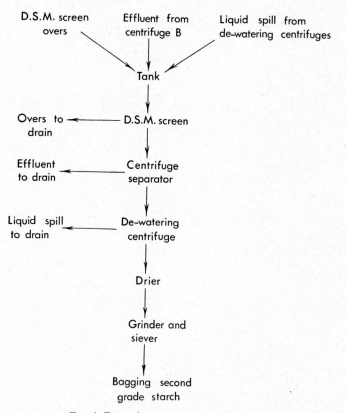

FIG. 4. Extraction process—stage 3.

solubles figure is very important, since a flour having a high value will usually give more trouble in production than will a flour with a low soluble value. More gluten break-up and impurer starch can be expected, quite apart from the obvious loss of material into the effluent.

6

The insoluble protein figure is not so important from the operating point of view (economically, of course, it is), except that there should be no sudden variation in the protein content of the flour being used. The plant will then be thrown out of step, having more starch and protein or less starch and more protein to pass through.

The golden rule is to aim for a constant flour supply, although this is very difficult when dealing with a material that varies from one season to the next, and doubly so when the plant happens to be in Australia, where the F.A.Q. (Fair Average Quality) system operates.

The manner in which different varieties of flour will vary is shown by these typical figures from a number of samples offered in England and considered for wheat-starch production.

Sample	Moisture	Insol. Protein	Sol. Protein	Other Sols.	Difference mainly Starch % w/w
S.A.	12·03	10·37	2·09	5·21	70·30
L.G.M.	13·44	12·49	1·81	4·34	67·92
R.A.	12·97	9·47	1·60	5·44	70·52
R.E.	13·80	7·34	1·29	4·15	73·42
R.C.6	12·74	5·96	4·88	5·52	70·90
R.C.1	13·32	6·65	1·22	3·04	75·77

The procedure for obtaining the above figures is dealt with in the chapter headed 'Laboratory Methods'.

An improved flour, for the purpose of starch extraction, can be obtained if normal milled flour is subjected to air classification and the fine fraction removed (1). These fines contain much of the low-grade starch which eventually finds its way into the factory effluent. The fine fraction is defined as smaller than 35 μ, and it would obviously be better to arrange that the flour-milling process produced a coarser type of flour in the first instance.

On the other hand, it is reported that the very fine protein-enriched fraction (15 μ and smaller) from the classifier presents an excellent raw material for gluten and starch processing, with a high yield of the available gluten recovered (2). This could be useful when wheat gluten is required without the normal accompanying proportion of starch.

Referring to the flowsheet (Fig. 2), it should be mentioned that the flour is fed to the dough mixer in a constant, weighed stream. This can be achieved by screw conveying from the flour storage bin into an electric vibrating feeder. This in turn feeds into a conveying weigh-belt which supplies the dough mixer. The system is so arranged that the weight of flour per foot of belt is indicated and any fluctuation of this weight causes an instantaneous adjustment of the vibrating feeder to ensure the maintenance of an accurate output (Fig. 5).

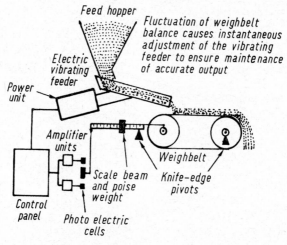

Fig. 5. Automatic weighing device.

Water. The water supply is passed through some metering device (e.g. rotameter) and fed into the dough mixer in the ratio of about 0·70 part of water to 1·0 part of flour by weight. This is to say that 1 long ton of flour requires 157 gallons of water. This ratio can vary from 0·6 : 1·0 up to 0·85 : 1·0, depending on the flour used.

The temperature of the water should be kept constant, this being particularly important in the hotter regions of the world, where the temperature of normal water supplies varies considerably throughout the year. A good temperature to aim for is 20°C. When the water temperature is a lot higher than this the dough becomes slacker and the gluten shows signs of fatigue, particularly under the action of beaters. A greater loss is incurred in the form of solubles, and the enzyme activity in the starch and gluten is much greater. The yield figures for the starch and gluten show an alarming fall when the system is at too high a temperature.

When the temperature of the water is too low the hydration of the gluten is slowed down and the dough will receive an insufficient period of washing under the normal conditions. This gives low starch yields and gluten of low protein content.

The hardness of the water supply is another important factor to be considered. It is known from experience that soft water is not suitable for this process. When soft water is used in the dough-making and the dough-washing operations, increased break-up and sliminess of the gluten is experienced. This can be overcome by the addition of sodium chloride. In one starch factory in Australia, which operates in an area which is serviced from a soft-water reservoir, special wells have been sunk to supply the necessary hard water for the dough-making and dough-washing operations.

It goes without saying that the water supply must be free from contamination and must be fresh. Flour and dough very quickly encourage the growth of bacteria and enzymic activity.

Dough mixing. The flour and water are fed into some device which will mix them intimately in a continuous fashion. A ribbon blender can be used in which the paddles are arranged so that efficient mixing takes place and the dough is gradually advanced towards the discharge end. The working of the dough by the paddle should not be excessive, but just sufficient to agglomerate the gluten. Baffles can be used to slow the advance of the dough so that the discharged material is of a smooth texture and free from lumps. It is best arranged that the water is spray-fed above the flour inlet, since this sort of arrangement will eliminate dust problems arising from the feed of flour.

The dough must be given a rest period to allow the gluten to hydrate fully and strengthen. Underdeveloped doughs tend to break into small pieces in the washing process and at least half an hour is required for the rest period. This can be achieved simply by feeding the dough into a hopper with sufficient capacity to allow the requisite time lag. For example, in a plant producing 10,000 lb. of dough per hour (6,000 lb. flour), the hopper should have a capacity of about 6,000 lb. of dough.

Dough extraction. Many devices have been suggested and constructed for the next stage, the extraction of the starch by washing. However, in the author's experience the simplest idea works best.

A deep, narrow, boat-shaped vessel with twin open-paddle rotors running the full length of the machine is a simple kind of arrangement that works well. Perforations or grooves on the sides of the rotor beds assist the action of the paddles, which are arranged to run in opposite directions, at different speeds (Fig. 6).

The dough is fed in one end, from the top, at such a rate that the solids in the bottom of the vessel just cover the paddles. This occupies about one-third of the depth. Water is forced into the vessel from points along the bottom, and bottom sides, at a known rate of flow. The liquid level of the extractor is controlled by the overflow points in the sides and this is the outlet for the starch slurry. The outlet for the gluten is at the bottom end of the vessel, furthest away from the dough inlet. The gluten fills the take-off pipe, which is controlled by a pump, and plugs the extractor, allowing very little of the starch to flow away. All conditions should be kept constant, the flow of dough in, the flow of water in at constant temperature, the flow of starch slurry out and the flow of gluten out. With these conditions the wet gluten leaving the extractor will contain at least 80% w/w protein (N × 5·7) on a dry basis. The wet gluten contains about 30% by weight as solids, the rest being water at this point, and it is good practice to carry out some simple pre-treatment before the material is fed into a drier. Passing it through a slow-moving set of rolls will reduce the water content by up to 10%, to about 60%, while the use

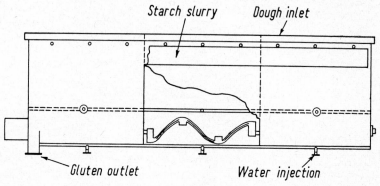

FIG. 6. Dough extractor.

of sodium chloride solutions can reduce the total water present to as low as 40%. However, some separation of the retained albumins and globulins is effected by this, and the gluten obtained is abnormal. The gluten tends to be short and granular and does not give a good performance in bread and baked goods. Yet for many purposes this gluten would be quite satisfactory although, of course, it contains free sodium chloride.

Gluten drying. Some observations in the difficulties of drying wheat gluten can be mentioned here. If the drying conditions are too severe (i.e. the temperature too high or the time period too long) then the end product is denatured to a larger extent than is acceptable for some of the uses of gluten. The dried gluten is always denatured to some degree, but the extent of this must be carefully controlled. Again, if the particles of gluten passing through the drier are too large, a surface drying will take place while the centre of the particle will still be wet. Gluten can be troublesome in sticking and agglomerating on the walls, and particularly so on the bends, of the drier.

One of the most popular, but not necessarily one of the best, ways of drying wet gluten is by means of a pneumatic ring-type drier. Several interesting alternative methods are described in the latter part of this chapter.

In the diagram (Fig. 7) the fan (a) is the only moving part of the drying system and produces a vigorous circular flow and continuous renewal of drying medium in the main ring (b). The inlet and outlet of the main system are combined in a manifold (c). Fresh hot air enters through (d), while the spent air is withdrawn through the centre of the manifold at (e). The wet gluten is fed through an extruder (f) into a disintegrator (j) which is placed at the lowest point of the ring duct in such a manner that the full circular flow of drying air and material passes right through it. The mixed material becomes airborne at once and is carried round the ring duct in floating contact with the hot-air stream. Owing to the intense rotary movement in the

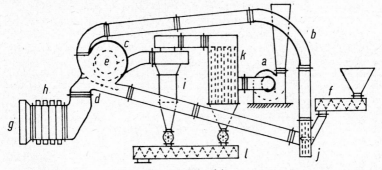

FIG. 7. Ring drier.

manifold (c), the main stream of material travels along the outer wall and continues to circulate in the ring duct, entrained and boosted on by the sharp jet of drying medium entering through injector (d). A heavy stream of material is thus kept in continuous circulation through the disintegrator, while a controllable fraction of lightest and driest particles will follow the air against the centrifugal force through the central outlet (e). The fresh drying medium is drawn into the plant through the filter (g) and heater (h). The method of heating is by individual choice, but is usually steam, gas or oil. The finished gluten is discharged through the separator (i) and the textile filters(k), to be combined in a worm forward mixer (l), and is ground, sieved and bagged off.

The finished product is a very fine, light-brown powder which contains about 10% w/w moisture and about 80% w/w protein (N × 5·7) on a dry solids basis. When reconstituted with water at 20°C, the characteristic properties of fresh gluten are exhibited and a coherent elastic and extensible mass is formed. It is evident that some denaturisation has taken place, but in a good gluten extraction process this is kept to a minimum.

11

TABLE 1
WHEAT STARCH SLURRIES
Specific gravity and concentration (3)

°Bé	Corresponding Sp. Gr. 20°/4°C	% Starch Dry Solids	Specific Gravity 20°/20°C	Gr. Starch Dry Solids in 100 c.c.
0·5	1·0034	0·90	1·0052	0·91
1·0	1·0069	1·81	1·0087	1·82
1·5	1·0104	2·71	1·0122	2·74
2·0	1·0140	3·61	1·0159	3·67
2·5	1·0175	4·52	1·0193	4·62
3·0	1·0211	5·42	1·0230	5·54
3·5	1·0248	6·32	1·0266	6·49
4·0	1·0285	7·22	1·0303	7·44
4·5	1·0325	8·13	1·0344	8·42
5·0	1·0358	9·03	1·0387	9·35
5·5	1·0395	9·93	1·0414	10·34
6·0	1·0433	10·94	1·0452	11·33
6·5	1·0470	11·72	1·0489	12·29
7·0	1·0508	12·64	1·0527	13·31
7·5	1·0546	13·55	1·0565	14·32
8·0	1·0585	14·45	1·0604	15·34
8·5	1·0624	15·35	1·0643	16·33
9·0	1·0663	16·25	1·0682	17·36
9·5	1·0702	17·16	1·0721	18·40
10·0	1·0742	18·06	1·0780	19·47
10·5	1·0782	18·96	1·0808	20·48
11·0	1·0822	19·87	1·0842	21·54
11·5	1·0862	20·77	1·0884	22·61
12·0	1·0903	21·67	1·0923	23·67
12·5	1·0944	22·58	1·0964	24·76
13·0	1·0986	23·48	1·1007	25·84
13·5	1·1028	24·38	1·1048	26·93
14·0	1·1071	25·28	1·1091	28·04
14·5	1·1113	26·18	1·1133	29·15
15·0	1·1156	27·09	1·1172	30·28
15·5	1·1199	27·99	1·1219	31·40
16·0	1·1242	28·89	1·1262	32·53
16·5	1·1286	29·80	1·1306	33·69
17·0	1·1330	30·70	1·1357	34·85
17·5	1·1374	31·60	1·1394	35·78
18·0	1·1419	32·50	1·1440	37·18
18·5	1·1464	33·41	1·1483	38·37
19·0	1·1510	34·31	1·1530	39·56
19·5	1·1556	35·21	1·1577	40·76
20·0	1·1602	36·12	1·1623	41·98
20·5	1·1659	37·02	1·1680	43·24
21·0	1·1696	37·93	1·1717	44·44
21·5	1·1743	38·83	1·1764	45·68
22·0	1·1791	39·73	1·1812	46·93
22·5	1·1839	40·64	1·1855	48·18
23·0	1·1888	41·54	1·1909	49·47
23·5	1·1937	42·44	1·1958	50·75
24·0	1·1986	43·34	1·2008	52·04
24·5	1·2036	44·25	1·2058	53·35

In order to convert the last columns into lb./Imperial gallons, the figures of that column have to be divided by 10. For U.S. gallons the figures have to be multiplied by 0·083.

TABLE 2

LOWER SPECIFIC GRAVITIES 0–5°Bé

°Bé	% Dry Solids	Specific Gravity 20°/20°C	Gr. Starch Dry Solids in 100 c.c.
0·2	0·36	1·0032	0·36
0·4	0·72	1·0045	0·72
0·6	1·08	1·0060	1·09
0·8	1·45	1·0073	1·46
1·0	1·81	1·0087	1·83
1·2	2·17	1·0102	2·19
1·4	2·53	1·0116	2·56
1·6	2·89	1·0130	3·00
1·8	3·26	1·0145	3·31
2·0	3·61	1·0159	3·67
2·2	3·98	1·0173	4·05
2·4	4·34	1·0187	4·42
2·6	4·70	1·0201	4·80
2·8	5·06	1·0210	5·17
3·0	5·42	1·0230	5·54
3·2	5·79	1·0244	5·93
3·4	6·15	1·0259	6·31
3·6	6·51	1·0273	6·69
3·8	6·88	1·0288	7·00
4·0	7·22	1·0303	7·44
4·2	7·60	1·0317	7·84
4·4	7·96	1·0332	8·22
4·6	8·31	1·0340	8·60
4·8	8·69	1·0361	9·01
5·0	9·03	1·0387	9·35

Stage 2 in Detail

Starch purification. The starch liquor coming from the extractor should be about 4°Bé or having a specific gravity of approximately 1·03 and containing 7·5 gm. of starch per 100 cm.[3]. The protein content (N × 5·7) of this liquor varies, but if the previous operations have been correctly carried out then the figure should not be in excess of 1·5% w/w calculated on the dry starch weight present, and more likely below 1·0% w/w.

There are several arrangements which work well for the purification of the starch slurry, but the one illustrated in Fig. 3 is considered simple and satisfactory.

Firstly the liquor must be sieved to free it from any large pieces of gluten and this can be done quite satisfactorily on a simple vibratory sieve fitted with a nylon cloth, British Standard Mesh No. 85, having an aperture opening of 0·178 mm. The vibratory action of the screen, which is inclined at about a 5° angle, is supplied by an eccentric shaft, an unbalanced flywheel, a cam and tappet arrangement, or an electromagnet. The feed on to the top of the cloth should be baffled to avoid flooding and channelling down the screen surface.

13

The coarse pieces of gluten which are the overs of the sieve can be sent direct to the gluten drier.

The throughs from the sieve should now be screened through a fine mesh, and this can be done very efficiently by means of a Dorr-Oliver D.S.M. screen. The features of this equipment are high

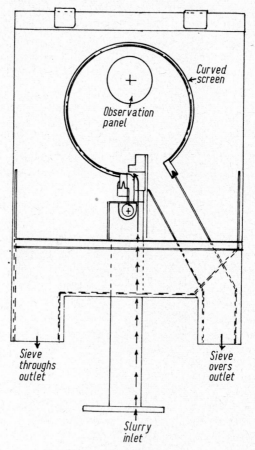

FIG. 8. Dorr-Oliver D.S.M. screen.

screening area capacity with no blinding of the screen, absence of moving parts, and low power consumption, while the floor space required is surprisingly small.

These screens were first developed by the Dutch State Mines to screen slurries in coal washeries and they are essentially a stationary curved screen made of wedge-shaped bars. The starch slurry is fed into the underside of the screen under pump pressure of over 30 lb. per sq. in., and the fine particles pass through while the coarse fraction passes round the underside of the screen and is discharged. The size of the screen required here is about 0·100 mm. aperture size. The D.S.M. screen is illustrated diagrammatically in Fig. 8.

The retained coarse fraction is now passed to the second-grade recovery system, the details of which are discussed later. The

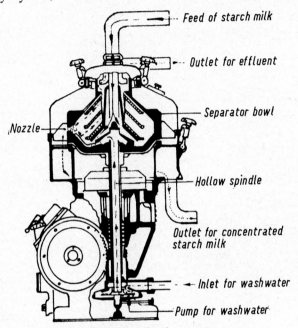

FIG. 9. Centrifugal separator.

throughs are collected in the regulator attached to the first centrifuge A.

The diagram (Fig. 9) shows the constructional principles of a continuous centrifugal starch separator. Separation takes place in the separator bowl, with rotation speeds varying according to the different models, from about 3,500 to 5,100 r.p.m. The separator spindle is driven by an electric motor via a V-belt drive, friction clutch and worm gear.

The starch milk is fed to the separator bowl from above and passes through the peripheral nozzles. A continuous flow of water is supplied through a central channel in the spindle while the separator is operating and is injected into the bowl through jets near the discharge nozzles.

The starch is thus washed by replacement of the original water with incoming pure water.

The two operations, washing and concentration of the starch, are carried out at the same time. The nozzle through-put is determined by the nozzle diameter and the bowl speed. If the feed of starch

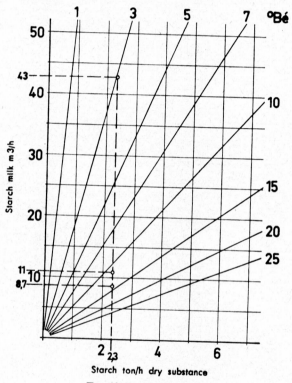

FIG. 10. De Laval graph.

slurry is greater than the through-put of the nozzles, then a concentration takes place (with washing), the grains of starch being forced out through the nozzles because of their greater density.

The accompanying diagram (Fig. 10) is used for the calculation of the volume of the starch concentrate in the starch separators manufactured by the De Laval Company of Sweden. From this calculation suitable nozzles in the bowl wall can be selected. The example shown is for Model TX 310–37 SH. Starch milk at a concentration

A) Bulk bins for flour storage.

B) Bulk transport of flour to starch factory.

PLATE ONE

of 3°Bé is supplied to the separator at the rate of 43 cu. m. per hour and is to be concentrated to 14°Bé. The diagram shows that the nozzle through-put must be about 8·7 cu. m. per hour, which for the standard bowl speeds corresponds to a nozzle diameter of 2·0 mm. 2·25 mm. would give a through-put of about 11 cu. m. an hour but a concentration of only about 11·5°Bé.

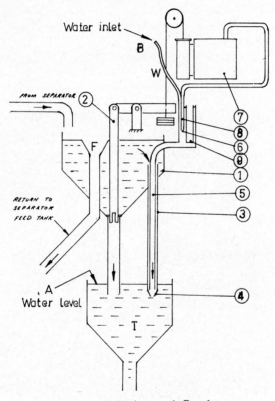

FIG. 11. Källe Automatic Regulator.

To get the best results at this centrifugal stage, which involves washing and concentrating of the starch, the machine must be fed with a starch slurry of constant specific gravity. Then if the machine is operated under constant speed and wash-water flow, the concentrate leaving the machine will be constant. In most starch factories variations will occur in the Baumé of the starch liquor feed, and to compensate for this a regulator is required. The Swedish Källe

Automatic Regulator is such a device and it measures the concentration of the starch concentrate from the centrifuge. Fluctuations in the concentrate are adjusted by the return of an amount of starch to the feed tank for the centrifuge. This alters the concentration of the feed so that a constant and predetermined concentration of the nozzle discharge from the machine is again obtained.

Referring to Fig. 11, the concentrate from the centrifuge is fed to tank (1). This tank, which is cone-shaped, is fitted in the bottom outlet with a regulating valve (2) consisting of a circular tube moving up and down in the circular opening. The tube is slotted so that the valve regulates the amount of starch passed on to the next stage in the purification scheme via the tank (T). There is an overflow funnel (F) in tank (1) by which the starch is returned to the centrifuge feed tank, and this compensates for any fluctuation in the concentrate from the centrifuge. With proper operation a small overflow of starch is always returning via the funnel (F).

Through the side of tank (1), a pipe (3) protrudes into tank (T) and terminates in a nozzle (4), which is just below the level of liquid in tank (T). A certain amount of starch will always flow through this pipe into (T) as well as through regulating valve (2). Inside this pipe (3) is another of smaller diameter (5) which in turn is connected to a tube (6). A trickle of water is constantly flowing into tube (6) through the pipe shown (W), and thus water and starch concentrate will flow out through the nozzle (4). Tank (1) with pipe (3) and tube (6) and also pipe (5) form a communicating pipe system. As the starch concentrate is heavier than water, the water level in pipe (6) will rise above the level of concentrate in tank (1). This level of concentrate in tank (1) is fixed by means of the overflow.

Variations in concentration (specific gravity) of the starch in tank (1) will appear as differences in the water level in tube (6). For a communicating pipe system having a water column of 2,900 mm., a variation of 1°Bé in the concentration corresponds to a difference in water level of about 20 mm.

In order to use this fluctuation in the water level, a pneumatic, hydraulically operating regulator (7) is used. This regulator receives its impulses through a pipe (8), the end of which protrudes into tube (6) under the water level. From the regulator some air is continuously pressed out through the pipe (8). The air pressure in the regulator will thus vary with the height of the water column in pipe (6) above the end of pipe (8). The air pressure then provides impulses to a hydraulically driven piston in the regulator by means of which the valve (2) is operated.

The position of the end of pipe (8) will determine the concentration of the starch concentrate discharged from the separator. Should the concentration be kept, for example, 2°Bé too low by the automatic controlling device, the position of the pipe (8) will have to be adjusted by raising it about 40 mm., whereafter the automatic controlling device will maintain the concentrate at a 2°Bé higher concentration.

The regulator is so designed that should, for example, the water level in pipe (6) move 1 mm., the piston of the regulator will move about the same distance. The regulator is then continued in the same direction until the water level has reached its original position and the concentration has reverted to its previous value. The speed of the piston of the regulator can be adjusted as desired.

Each concentration of starch slurry in tank (1) corresponds to a certain water level in tube (6). The water level in tube (6) can thus be graduated in Baumé. For this reason a sight glass (9) is connected to tube (6) so that the water level can be observed, and a scale graduated in Baumé can be placed behind the sight glass.

The principal objective in the separation scheme at this first stage (A) is to get the starch well washed and to concentrate it to a degree such that only protein and other impurities are lost in the effluent, but no starch. The effluent can then be passed directly to the effluent recovery system. By doing this the concentrated starch will contain some undesirable impurities, but this is taken care of in the next stage (B). The concentration of the starch concentrate will vary from factory to factory, but 12°Bé (about 23·7 gm. starch per 100 cm.³) is a reasonable figure. This is now diluted with water and controlled again by a Källe regulator to feed about 10°Bé (about 19·5 gm. starch per 100 cm.³) into centrifuge B. This is the same type of machine as A, and washes and concentrates the starch stream. The operation at this stage is to concentrate the starch to a high degree, making sure that the impurities are thrown over into the effluent. This means that a proportion of starch is present in the effluent, but also that the starch concentrate is pure. The effluent from this stage is passed to the second-grade starch system. The concentrated starch stream will be about 16°Bé (about 32·5 gm. starch per 100 cm.³) and should not contain more than 0·3% w/w protein (N × 5·7) calculated on the weight of dry starch present. Preferably the figure is 0·2% w/w.

The next stage is the de-watering of the starch stream, and this is best and most conveniently done on an automatic horizontal centrifuge of the solid basket type. The diameter of the basket may be as large as 65 in., and with the automatic cutting out and unloading while operating at speed, it means that two bearing supports of great rigidity are necessary (Fig. 12).

The starch slurry is automatically fed in from the feed tank when the basket has attained the correct speed (for a 65-in. diameter basket this is 750–800 r.p.m.) and continues to flow in at a high constant rate of feed. The speed of the centrifuge is kept constant throughout all the operations. A take-off pipe is fitted inside the basket and this takes off the spun liquor from the turbulent zone containing the lighter fragments of impurity and starch which have not been thrown to the side of the basket. In one type of machine the take-off pipe is arranged to operate initially in a position close to the wall of the basket and then automatically to recede as the starch cake

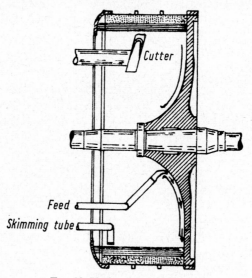

FIG. 12. Horizontal centrifuge.

builds up. At the end of the cycle the pipe remains stationary while the starch feed continues to give a period of overflow. This is to cut down the slime layer which tends to collect on the top of the starch cake.

The liquor which passes through the take-off pipe is pumped over to the second-grade starch system.

While the basket is still spinning, a knife cuts out the spun starch and this is arranged to fall directly into a screw conveyor. The starch cake contains about 40% w/w moisture and is now ready for the final drying.

Starch drying. Not all types of driers are suitable for dealing with this starch cake. Cooking of the starch and hard grit formation can occur if the temperature, contact time, and dispersion are not correct.

A pneumatic so-called 'flash' drier is the type usually favoured and an example of this is illustrated in Fig. 13.

The plant consists of a vertical column which converges to the feed

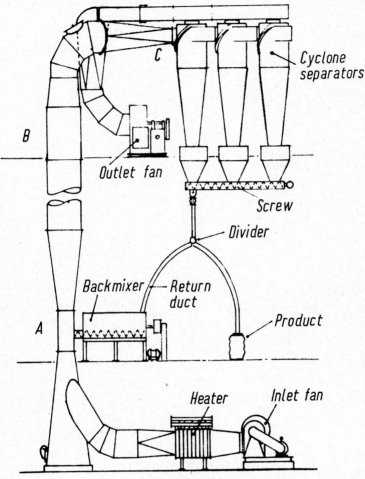

FIG. 13. Flash drier.

point (A) and then diverges in a gentle taper to a regular section (B). The column finally converges again to a duct leading to the starch separating equipment (C). By this means a high velocity is maintained at the feed point in order to ensure that the material is airborne, and the diameter of the column is then increased to reduce the velocity, and hence prolong the time of contact, between the material and the hot air until the velocity reaches a minimum in the main section (B). It is in this section that most of the water is evaporated. From the top of section (B) the column converges again and the velocity is increased, readily conveying the starch to cyclones.

The system is provided with two air-circulating fans, the first of which is situated before the heater (steam or oil). Air is forced through the heater into the bottom of the drying column, where it meets the flow of feed material being screwed from the back-mixer. The back-mixer is fed with wet cake and dry return in the ratio of about 60 : 40 by weight. The second fan is situated after the cyclones and draws the air out of the drying column. These two fans must, of course, be balanced, and the ducting connecting the two fans is provided with dampers. Under operating conditions these are adjusted so that the delivery pressure from the inlet fan and the suction of the outlet fan give a value equal to atmospheric pressure, or very slight suction, at the starch feed point. This means that there is no blow-out of feed material and the ingress of cold air is minimised. The column is constructed of mild steel. The plant should be fitted with the usual recording instruments to give temperature and pressure readings.

The dried starch is now sieved and the coarse fraction ground to the required size and the whole is bagged off. The starch in the bag is of high quality, with a moisture content of about 12% w/w and a protein content of 0·2% w/w dry basis.

Stage 3 in Detail

Second-grade starch. The effluent from the Dorr-Oliver D.S.M. screens, the effluent from the second-pass continuous centrifuges, and the take-off liquor from the de-watering centrifuge all pass to a recovery tank for processing into second-grade starch. This system ensures that there is no return liquid into the main starch process, and this is very desirable to avoid concentration of impurities within the main system.

The collected liquors should now be sieved to remove any large and undesirable aggregates and this can be done in another Dorr-Oliver D.S.M. screen. The underside overs of the screen are discharged to the drain while the sieved liquors are processed in another of the continuous centrifuges, this time in such a manner that the total solids are scavenged from the liquors. The clear liquid is discharged to drain while the starch concentrate is fed to a small de-watering centrifuge. This centrifuge will be smaller in size than the equipment used in the main starch line, and indeed the operation can be done batchwise. A suitable machine for this would be the standard type centrifuge in

A) Part of a starch slurry purification system.

B) A battery of D.S.M. screens.

PLATE TWO

general use in the chemical industry and having overhead suspension and bottom discharge (Fig. 14).

The thick slurry is fed from above into the perforated basket, which is started from rest and rotated at moderate speeds while being loaded.

After the basket is full, the rotation is increased to the maximum and held there for about 15 minutes. Surrounding the basket is a monitor curb with an annular gutter at the bottom, provided with a discharge pipe. The mother liquor, or in this case clear waste liquor, is forced through the perforations in the basket, strikes the casing wall, runs down to the gutter and escapes to drain. The basket is lined with a metal wire screen in order to increase the drainage surface. Against the screen there is fixed a filter cloth, a fine nylon mesh.

After the drying period the centrifuge is retarded and stopped and a broad annular valve which forms part of the bottom is lifted and hung out of the way. The spun starch can now be dug out and discharged through the bottom space into a discharge shute or conveyor.

The starch cake containing about 40% w/w moisture can now be dried in a pneumatic flash drier, as already described. The final starch will contain about 12% w/w moisture and protein content varying between 0·6% w/w and 1·0% w/w (N × 5·7) on a dry solids basis. This product is described as second-grade starch and it is used in products in which the high protein is not important.

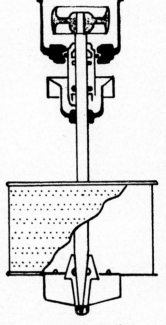

FIG. 14. Bowl centrifuge, suspended type.

Weight Calculations

The following weight balances for the production of starch and gluten were obtained on a pilot plant which was operated on much the same scheme as the one that has been outlined in this chapter. The figures were obtained when steady conditions had been achieved in the plant and covered a duration of several hours running. Large commercial plants are also obtaining these kinds of yield.

Run 1. Using an English-type flour with the following analysis:

		% w/w	
	Moisture	12·03	
(Soluble Protein 2·09% w/w)	Insoluble Protein	10·37	(N × 5·7)
	Total Solubles	7·30	
	Carbohydrate	70·30	(by difference)
		100·00	

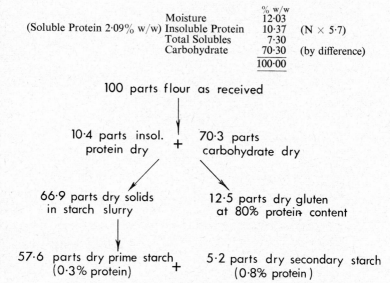

100 parts flour as received

10·4 parts insol. protein dry + 70·3 parts carbohydrate dry

66·9 parts dry solids in starch slurry

12·5 parts dry gluten at 80% protein content

57·6 parts dry prime starch (0·3% protein) + 5·2 parts dry secondary starch (0·8% protein)

Thus the recovered dry solids amount to 93% overall, and 87% is the figure for recovered dry solids as prime products. The proportion of the total insoluble carbohydrates recovered as prime starch is 82%, while the proportion of insoluble protein recovered in the gluten is 96%.

The commercial yields of prime starch at 12% moisture and gluten at 10% moisture from the flour as received are respectively 65% and 14%.

Run 2. Using a Manitoba flour with the following analysis:

		% w/w	
	Moisture	13·44	
(Soluble Protein 1·8% w/w)	Insoluble Protein	12·49	(N × 5·7)
	Total Solubles	6·15	
	Carbohydrate	67·92	(by difference)
		100·00	

Thus the recovered dry solids are 95% overall and 89% as prime products. The proportion of the insoluble carbohydrates as prime starch is 83%, while the proportion of protein recovered is again 96%.

The commercial yield of prime starch at 12% moisture is 64% and that of gluten at 10% moisture is 17% based on the flour as received. The moisture of the Manitoba flour when used was higher than that of the English flour in the first example.

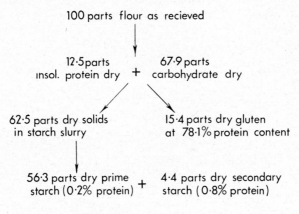

STARCH FACTORY EFFLUENT

In a wheat-starch factory the liquid effluent is a problem which must be faced up to and dealt with energetically. Quite apart from the large volume of effluent that is produced by a big factory, the nature of the liquid creates problems.

The solid content is variable, but is about 1% w/v, and of these solids roughly half will be in solution and half in suspension. Proteins, pentosans, starch, sugars and inorganic salts are all present, together with enzymes, and thriving colonies of micro-organisms. Decomposition of the starch and gluten takes place rapidly, and static pools of the effluent soon become foul, bubbling and evil smelling.

The outgoing of the effluent represents a substantial loss from the original flour, in the order of 10% by weight. From the work done in many laboratories it would seem also that this fraction is a valuable one so far as baking performance of the gluten is concerned. However, the recovery of this effluent fraction is not economical unless much surplus steam is available, coupled with the necessary equipment, e.g. spray driers.

The effluent can be concentrated up to about 25% solids by using a continuous centrifugal scavenger, and the resulting material is extremely thick and viscous, indeed being so stiff that it will not run away by gravity. The main reason for this seems to be the high pentosan content which exhibits very high swelling properties, thus giving a gel-like structure to the liquid.

This concentrate alone can be dried on roller-drum driers or it can be mixed with flour or starch and dried. It can also be spray-dried under pressure, or at atmospheric pressure, in a more dilute form.

A better approach to the recovery of the effluent is probably its use for biological protein synthesis. It can be used to cultivate yeast.

Torulopsis utilis, which is commonly called Torula yeast, is a very suitable material for the production of a food yeast from most waste liquors. It has a resistance to contamination by other organisms when the pH is held to 5 or below, and produces a palatable product which is high in protein and vitamin content. It has been used both as a high protein food and as a vitamin B complex supplement.

Torula yeast is grown under aerobic conditions and at temperatures of about 30°C. The growth rate depends on the accessibility of food and oxygen and upon the constant removal of carbon dioxide. The generation time of this strain should be less than 100 minutes, and 1 kg. of the yeast requires 0·4386 kg. sugar, 0·00526 kg. phosphorus and 0·02113 kg. nitrogen. For each 1 lb. of sugar oxidised there is liberated 1600 B.T.U. The propagation usually takes place in a cell container in which some device supplies the necessary aeration of the liquid contents. Air may be added by a stationary system such as a jet tube or a porcelain filter candle. On the other hand a rotating system may be used, but whichever air system is used, a steady supply of finely divided air in excess of the growth needs is the basic requirement. Foaming is experienced, and is usually controlled by anti-foam chemicals or by some mechanical beating device.

The process can be batchwise or continuous. In the batch process it is usual to find initially a very slow rate of growth while the organism acclimatises itself; after this the reaction speeds up. Under continuous conditions there is uniform addition and withdrawal of liquid, and the yeast will have a certain average holding time in the reactor cell. This residence time is calculated as the ratio of the active reactor volume to the feed rate. A series of reactors is more efficient than one large cell. At optimum conditions a residence time of about 4 hours can be expected from this type of feed and material.

Wheat starch factory effluent is very suitable for this type of process. A similar use for the factory wastes from potato starch production has been described (4).

The water substrate contained about 1·2% solids, which consisted of 37% protein, 12% sugar and 0·8% starch. The solution had a 5-day B.O.D. (biological oxygen demand) averaging 7,720 p.p.m. Phosphorus, potassium and calcium were present in ample amounts. Swift's inedible defoamer No. 1000 was found to be effective in controlling foam and gave yeast growths many times greater than the substrate with no defoamer. A culture of *Torulopsis utilis* NRRL Y-900 was used. An aeration rate of 1·2 volumes per solution volume, per minute, and a stirring rate of 400 r.p.m. was used, with the temperature between 30°C and 32°C. The preferred pH was 5 and at this value *Torulopsis utilis* remained the dominant strain. The percentage of the initial solids recovered through the yeast growth was 45% as the economic optimum, because it showed both a high rate of recovery and a recovery of only about 5% below the maximum. The holding time was 4 hours, this being the per cent solids recovery divided by the per cent recovery per hour. The yeast obtained had a protein content of 55% dry solids basis (N × 6·25) and was recovered as a semi-solid containing approximately 85% water. The reduction in the 5-day B.O.D. figure of the effluent was about 60%.

One starch factory situated in an industrially remote area of Australia and having no conventional outlet for effluent disposal has solved the problem in an enterprising manner. The effluent is piped about a mile to a farm where it is allowed to flow into holding tanks. After a short period of settlement the supernatant liquid is used for spray irrigation around the farm property. The settlement in the tanks is periodically dug out and used in pig and cattle feeding.

Alternative Methods of Production

The manufacturing procedure described in the previous section is based on the Martin process, and this is widely practised. However, other methods exist for the extraction of starch and gluten, and several of these will be described.

(1) *The continuous batter process.* During the Second World War this process was developed by the Northern Utilisation Research and Development Division of the U.S. Department of Agriculture. The important difference between this process and the Martin process lies in the treatment of the matured dough. In the Batter process this is dispersed in water and the divided gluten particles recovered on a sieve.

In a comparatively recent paper (5) the operation of this method on a continuous pilot plant is described. The flowsheet is shown in (Fig. 15).

The above paper describes the details: 'Wheat flour and water are fed continuously at controlled rates to the feed end of an Abbé double spiral ribbon blender, in which the outer spiral blade carries material to the discharge end of the mixer while the inner blade works it back. The ratio of water to flour ranges between 0·7 to 1 and 1·8 to 1, depending upon the type of flour used. For a flour milled from a soft wheat the ratio of water to flour ranges between 0·7 to 1 and 1·2 to 1, whereas with flours from hard wheats the ratio ranges from 1·2 to 1 to 1·6 to 1. Flours of very high protein content may require a ratio of water to flour as high as 1·8 to 1. Water at a temperature of

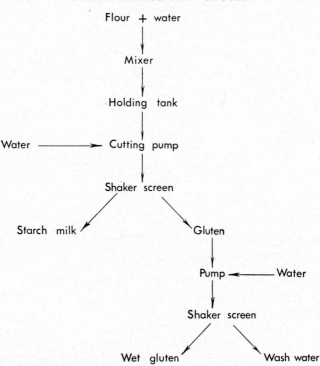

FIG. 15. Batter process flowsheet.

120°–135°F is used to facilitate hydration of the gluten and to reduce the mixing time necessary for producing a batter of proper consistency. The temperature of the batter during mixing is usually about 110°F. After a short retention time in the mixer the batter is in a suitable condition for washing. If the flour has been milled from soft wheat a long retention time may be required, and this can be provided in the mixer itself, or in a separate agitated tank for additional holding or ageing.

'The batter is then passed to a Jabsco pump, called the "cutting pump", together with sufficient cold water to give a ratio of water to flour in the mixture at this point ranging from 2 : 1 to 5 : 1. Here the batter is intimately contacted with wash water by agitation of the pump impeller. Thus starch is washed from the gluten, which remains in the form of small curds. Slurry from the cutting pump is screened on a Rotex shaker. The curds of gluten are separated continuously from the starch milk on a screen of 60–150 mesh, depending upon the flour being processed. Wash water is sprayed on the separated gluten

PLATE THREE

A) De-watering centrifuge.

B) Pilot plant spray drier.

as it moves down the screen. Gluten recovered in this primary separation stage may have a protein content as high as 65% dry basis.

'The screened gluten is washed by pumping it, with added water, to a second shaker screen. Protein content of the gluten recovered after the second washing stage is in the range of 75–80% dry basis.'

The resulting products are starch slurry and wet gluten, and the starch slurry can be purified and the gluten dried as described in the previous section on the Martin process.

The results obtained in this pilot plant are summarised in the following table included in the account.

Flour Compositions	A	B	C	D	E	F
Protein % MFB	9·2	11·2	14·3	14·6	16·6	17·9
Ash % MFB	0·39	0·34	0·41	0·41	0·79	1·13
Solubles % MFB	5·1	4·9	6·3	6·3	7·4	8·9
Operating Data						
Flour feed lb. MFB	96·2	88·6	87·2	87·2	86·7	84·6
Total mixing lb./lb. dry flour	0·86	0·90	1·11	1·11	1·17	1·55
Cutting water lb./lb. dry flour	1·56	1·41	1·44	1·44	1·44	1·48
First screen mesh	150	150	150	150	150	60
Second screen mesh	100	100	100	100	100	60
Products						
Gluten fraction lb. (wet)	25·0	35·0	44·5	50·0	48·0	52·5
Solids %	33·4	36·4	35·1	35·2	37·6	31·5
Protein % MFB	81·0	81·0	80·7	79·6	83·7	76·4
Starch milk, gal.	76·5	60·0	56·5	54·9	56·5	68·6
Solids lb./gal.	0·95	1·01	0·97	0·98	0·98	0·86
Protein lb./gal.	0·021	0·019	0·022	0·024	0·028	0·038
Wash water, gal.	130	150	138	118	148	175
Solids lb./gal.	0·098	0·083	0·133	0·146	0·107	0·033
Protein lb./gal.	0·0066	0·0030	0·0054	0·0044	0·0053	0·0025
Recoveries						
Solids recovery % MFB	97·0	94·1	98·8	97·2	98·7	95·3
Protein in gluten/total protein in flour	72·1	84·0	84·1	85·9	83·6	80·0

A = Patent, soft white winter wheat   B = Patent, soft red winter wheat
C = Patent, hard red winter wheat   D = Patent, hard red spring wheat
E = First clear, hard red winter wheat   F = Second clear, hard red winter
MFB = moisture free basis   wheat
100 mesh = 0·0065 in. aperture   60 mesh = 0·0092 in. aperture
Protein is estimated as N% × 5·7   150 mesh = 0·0041 in. aperture

This process has been described as an improved method for processing wheat flour into starch and gluten, but in the author's opinion this is very doubtful. The basic principle of dispersing the gluten, rather than consolidating in the mass, can cause many problems in large-scale production. Claims for this process lie in the use of simpler machinery together with less power requirement. The use of less water in the extraction stage is mentioned and this could mean the economical recovery of the solubles fraction in the factory effluent. Taking this particular aspect of the process, it is interesting to examine more closely the figures in the above table of results. The concentrations of starch in the starch slurries range from 12·2 gm. of starch per 100 cm.³ of liquor to 10·4 gm. per 100 cm.³. This is a higher concentration than the 4°Bé (7·5 gm. per 100 cm.³) obtained in the modified Martin process. However, this 4°Bé liquor contains the total water used to produce wet gluten which contains 80% protein (d.s.b.). Therefore, to make a direct comparison of water usage, the gluten wash water shown in the above table must be added to the volume of the starch slurry. This wash water was presumably the water used to wash the initial gluten at 65% protein content to bring it up to a protein content of a more reasonable level. When this total figure is worked out the solids content falls to 5 gm. per 100 cm.³ or less (2·5°Bé), which is considerably lower than the 7·5 gm. per 100 cm.³ mentioned in the Martin process previously described. It is hard to see from these figures that the volume of water required in the Batter process is less than that in other processes, but when process water is re-used as gluten wash water, then this will be so.

As an example of the difficulties which can be met with when gluten is dispersed in the starch slurry, one notes the protein level of the starch milk shown in the table of results. This is in excess of 2% w/w calculated on the dry starch weight, and is too high.

The recovery of the protein as wet gluten is shown as a percentage of the total flour protein (presumably this includes soluble protein which is not recoverable) and ranges from 72·1% to 85·9%. The yields of pure starch are not given. In a very recent publication (6) describing generally the operation of the Batter process, the crude, moisture-free starch recovery (average 3% protein and including wash water solids) from 100 lb. of commercial flour, ranged from 67·7% to 76·5%. The moisture-free gluten recovery from the same amount of flour ranged from 7·0% to 16·6%, with the protein content of the gluten varying from 74·9% to 84·8% on a moisture-free basis.

(2) *The alkali method.* This is an example of a chemical method of separation rather than the previous purely physical methods. The fact that alkalis have a dispersing and dissolving action upon wheat protein has been used to separate pure starch from wheat flour. Sodium hydroxide is the preferred alkali in an aqueous concentration, sufficient to give a pH of about 11·5 when dispersed into a slurry with flour. Using 0·03N NaOH solution fulfils these requirements, and the total protein content of the flour is dissolved or dispersed sufficiently to prevent settling out on standing.

For an industrial process the following flowsheet can be suggested (Fig. 16).

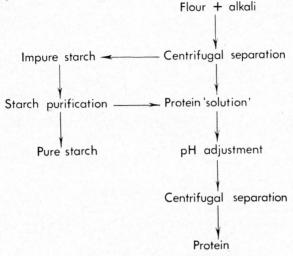

Flour + alkali

Impure starch ← Centrifugal separation

Starch purification → Protein 'solution'

Pure starch   pH adjustment

Centrifugal separation

Protein

FIG. 16. Alkali process flowsheet.

Flour is mixed into 0·1% w/v caustic soda solution in the ratio of 1 lb. of flour to 1 gal. of solution and stirred for about half an hour at room temperature (15°–20°C). A slurry of specific gravity 1·030 (4°Bé) and pH 11·44 is obtained.

This slurry is now spun in a solid bowl centrifuge or a perforated bowl lined with a suitable filter cloth. When a solid bowl is used the rate of feed is adjusted to give a clear spill over the rim of the bowl. In the case of a perforated bowl the feed must be slow enough to allow the filtrate to get away. The solid starch cake is then cut out and redispersed in caustic solution again, the whole operation being repeated. At this point the starch is redispersed in water and washed and concentrated in a continuous centrifugal separator in the usual starch circuit. From here it is de-watered and dried as described in the previous section of this chapter. The resulting starch is very pure, containing only about 0·15% protein on a dry basis (N × 5·7).

The behaviour of this starch when gelatinised is interesting in comparison with the wheat starch extracted by the purely physical methods. It swells and gelatinises at a lower temperature and gives a more translucent gel. The peak viscosity value is higher but the breakdown in viscosity with time is more pronounced and severe.

The recovery of starch represents about 85% of the available carbohydrate present.

31

The combined alkali extracts are now acidified with hydrochloric acid to pH 5·0 and stirred for half an hour. The precipitated protein can be filtered or is recovered in a perforated bowl centrifuge, preferably after having been concentrated in a centrifugal separator. The protein sludge is now dried in a flash drier. An extra yield of protein can be obtained by raising the temperature of the acidified extract to near boiling point, but this is not economical unless very cheap energy is available.

The dried gluten obtained by this method is denatured to a large degree and therefore cannot be used where vital wheat gluten is required. The yield of protein obtained is between 60% and 65% of the available, and this represents a poor return.

Dimler, Davis, Rist & Hilbert (7) studied the processing conditions for preparing starch and protein from flour by alkali treatment. They made measurements of the protein dispersing power of solutions of sodium, potassium, calcium and barium hydroxides, and of sodium carbonate on a soft wheat flour.

Alkali		Apparent Solubility %	pH
NaOH	0·03N	101	11·8
KOH	0·03N	100	11·7
NaOH	0·01N	95	10·9
KOH	0·01N	98	10·8
Ca(OH)$_2$	0·05N	92	11·7
Ba(OH)$_2$	0·05N	90	11·7
Na$_2$CO$_3$	0·3%	66	10·3

The above table shows that sodium or potassium hydroxide is the most efficient. An extension of this work was the determination of the relationship between the apparent solubility of the protein and the pH of the mixture of aqueous sodium hydroxide and flour. For any given flour the pH of the mixture appeared to be primarily dependent on the ratio of flour to sodium hydroxide and was influenced only to a minor extent by variations in the amount of water. For a maximum dispersion of flour protein the mixture should have a pH above 10·5, while a value of about 11·5 would give complete protein dispersion.

Dimler and his co-workers investigated the effect of pH on the extent of precipitation of wheat protein by acidification of the alkaline extract with sulphuric acid and came to the conclusion that pH 5·5 was the practical value to work at in the recovery process.

The alkali extraction process might prove useful for special purposes, as for example when samples of highly purified starch are required, and when there are no requirements for the protein to be recovered. However, in general the process is not of industrial significance, although it was reported (8) that a plant was operating this process in Canada. No details or yields were given.

EXPERIMENTAL METHODS

Dough Washing

Various methods for washing the matured dough in the Martin process have been suggested. Most of them are variations on the double spiral ribbon blender type of machine, with various arrangements for making the extraction of starch continuous.

An interesting method which has been investigated (9) is the use of a ball mill. The work was carried out on a laboratory scale only and using a small porcelain mill of about 1,100 ml. capacity. The number of porcelain balls was 68, each ball having an average volume of 3·6 ml. The mill was revolving at 128 r.p.m.

The matured dough (rested for 1 hour), made from a low-grade Manitoba flour (A) and water, in the proportion 1 : 0·75, was subjected to various times of milling in the presence of excess water at 15°C. After this time the starch slurry was poured off and examined. The most favourable conditions were found to be:

100 gm. of flour and 75 ml. of water mixed to a dough and matured at rest for 1 hour. Ball milling was carried out for one hour and gave gluten with a protein (N $\times$ 5·7) content of 76–80% w/w dry basis, with starch slurry of 0·7–0·9% protein calculated on the dry starch weight present. The volume of water used in the mill for washing was 500 ml. It is interesting to note that this process for the extraction of starch is much more economical in the use of water than is either the Martin or the Batter process.

Flour A	%w/w
Moisture	= 13·44
Insol. Protein	= 12·49
Total Soluble	= 6·15
Carbohydrate	= 67·92

The factors which have an influence on the efficiency of this process are flour strength, maturing time, milling time and temperature of milling.

(a) The flour strength determines the ratio of water required in the dough and the length of time of milling. A very weak flour would require the addition of sodium chloride to tighten up the dough, while a very strong flour could be modified by the raising of the ratio of water in the dough. Much the same considerations are required here as in the Martin process.

(b) Maturing time. Within limits, the longer the maturing time, the lower in protein content is the starch slurry. Above the limit, the gluten becomes too tough and requires too long a milling time or heavier balls. One hour was found to be a suitable compromise.

(c) The milling time is again the result of a compromise. It has to be sufficient to free the starch from the gluten but not sufficient to break the gluten down to give a high protein content in the starch slurry. The weight of the milling balls is interchangeable to some degree with milling time. The heavier the balls the shorter the milling time, within limits. One hour was the convenient and efficient period found.

(d) Temperature of the washing water is all-important, and the higher the temperature the quicker the release of starch. For good products, however, it is better to use water at 15°C or up to 20°C, since at higher temperatures larger amounts of material are taken into solution and gluten break-up is emphasised.

This method of dough washing can be made continuous, although it is perhaps primarily a batchwise method. In the work carried out the balls were easily removed from the gluten mass and showed no tendency to stick or become covered with gluten.

It is interesting to speculate on the use of a vibration mill for the above purpose. This type of mill could probably produce the gluten in one mass, as with the conventional ball mill, or in the form of divided particles suitable for the Batter process, with the use of very little water.

Gluten Drying

Most of the commercially produced vital gluten is dried in a form of flash or ring drier, and there exist many modifications of this type of drier, each of which is supposed to produce a better end product than the other. The truth of the matter is that there are several methods available for drying gluten which give a superior product to that obtained by flash drying. These and other methods will now be described.

(a) *Vacuum drying.* This was one of the first methods employed and produced a good, vital gluten because the wet gluten was only subjected to a low temperature. However, the method has never been adapted for economic commercial use because so much manpower is required and the cost of maintaining a low vacuum is excessive. The wet gluten must be cut into small pieces, or extruded into short worm-like pieces, and these are loaded into trays. When the drying is taking place the gluten pieces bubble up and swell, so that sufficient room must be left in the trays for this expansion. When the gluten is dry the trays must be emptied and the gluten can then be crushed and ground.

34

A) Wheat starch ($\times$ 360).

B) Double-drum drier.

PLATE FOUR

The resultant gluten is of a light colour and retains most of its original vitality.

(b) *Spray drying*. To be able to spray-dry wet gluten, it must be dispersed to a liquid consistency, so that this can be pumped into the nozzle unit, and thus dried in a fine state. Several agents have been used for the dispersion, and they include ammonia, carbon dioxide and organic acids such as acetic acid.

Ammonia. Wet gluten is introduced into an aqueous solution of ammonia in sufficient concentration to give a final slurry containing about 10% gluten solids. Sufficient ammonium hydroxide must be present to give a mixture pH of 9–10, and this is then subjected to vigorous agitation for sufficient time to get a homogeneous, free-flowing, light-yellow dispersion with the consistency of medium cream. This free-flowing, non-adhesive form is maintained for as long as the pH of 9–10 is maintained.

The dispersion is now atomised into a spray chamber to give the desired fineness in the finished product, which is a white powder containing about 6% moisture and with a good performance in baking tests. No residual ammonia is present in the end product.

The Blaw-Knox Company of the U.S.A. has developed this process (10). It was reported that a commercial installation was operating in Kansas.

Carbon dioxide. The use of carbon dioxide under superatmospheric pressure for the dispersion of wet gluten in water is the subject of a patent (11). Apparently the action of the weak carbonic acid on the gluten is similar to that of several organic acids. An example of this process is quoted: 45 gal. of water are introduced into a closed container of 55-gal. capacity together with 100 lb. of wet gluten (33% solids). Carbon dioxide was introduced with agitation and 2 lb. 7 oz. of the gas under 30 lb. pressure was needed to obtain a milky dispersion. This dispersion was then spray-dried to give small beads and flakes of dry gluten. The carbon dioxide was lost during this process and the final product was substantially vital.

Acetic acid. This acid has often been used to get a wet gluten-in-water dispersion. The solids content of a dispersion can vary from 10% to 25%, but at the higher end of the range the material is only semi-liquid and not very mobile. The best range for spray drying is about 10% to 14% solids, and the dispersion can be effected quickly by any machine which will give reasonable agitation.

The material is spray-dried in the normal way and a light-coloured powder is obtained with good reconstitution properties, which gives a good performance in baking tests. The finished product contains a residue of acetic acid, which is fairly evident by taste and smell, but

35

this is no drawback to its use in bread. However, it is not a good selling point. McConnell (12) reported that gluten dispersed in 0·01N acetic acid, pH near 5·4 and solids between 8% and 9%, and spray-dried with inlet temperature of drier at 160°C and an outlet temperature at 90°C gave a finished product comparable with freeze-dried gluten.

(c) *Drum-drying.* In the foregoing section on spray drying, the described liquid dispersions of the gluten in water can also be employed for drum-drying. Ammonia, carbon dioxide and acetic acid are all suitable agents for this purpose. Either double-drum or single-drum driers can be used, but conditions should be arranged so that there is no boiling reservoir between the rolls, since this prolonged contact time at high temperature will cause denaturation to take place. The dispersion should be fed on to the rolls by a travelling feed which coats the rolls from end to end. This can be arranged if the feed pipe is connected to the shaft of one of the rolls so that the outlet end of the pipe reciprocates from one end of the rolls to the other end and back during each revolution of the rolls. The rotational speed of the rolls should be as high as possible in order to keep the contact time of the gluten with the hot roll as small as possible.

An interesting description of the production of vital wheat gluten by drum-drying was published in *Cereal Chemistry*, 1958 (13). This paper describes drum-drying of wet gluten from dispersion in very dilute acid and with the use of a small pilot-plant drum drier. The variables investigated were the dispersion methods, pH, type of acid used, drying temperature, solids content, and type of flour from which the gluten was obtained. It was shown that when the gluten was thoroughly dispersed, as it was with the Waring Blender machine, the resulting dispersion could be drum-dried with little loss of baking strength, acetic acid solubility, and dough-expansion properties. The optimum pH of a dispersion in acetic acid was dependent upon the type of flour from which the gluten was obtained and also upon the concentration of the gluten in the dispersion. With a lower gluten concentration in the dispersion a higher pH could be tolerated to yield the same quality of gluten. Results indicated that most glutens prepared from clear and patent flours could be drum-dried from acetic acid in the pH range of 4·5 to 5·1, but that some optimum value exists for each gluten. Although hydrochloric, phosphoric and lactic acids were found to be suitable for gluten dispersion and subsequent drum-drying, acetic acid was preferred because of its acceptance in food products. It was also reported in this paper that the quality of the drum-dried gluten was practically independent of the operating steam pressure in the drums between 25 p.s.i.g. to 85 p.s.i.g., and that using acetic acid dispersions containing between 10% and 16% gluten gave the best results. The maximum output from the drums was 1·4 lb. of product per hour per square foot of drum area when drying to a 16·5% dispersion of gluten in acetic acid.

(d) *Freeze-drying*. With the wide interest that is being shown in the use of freeze-drying methods for food processing, it is interesting to know that gluten dried in this manner shows little loss of baking properties and produces a very good loaf of bread.

If wet gluten is extruded in the form of a thin rod this can be efficiently and continuously frozen. After a rapid and coarse grinding the granules can be effectively freeze-dried. The resulting gluten is light-coloured and of good quality.

Dry ice mixed in with wet gluten can be ground and treated in the same way.

Adams (14) reported on the use of dry ice and liquid nitrogen before freezing the wet gluten to produce a white, good-quality, dry gluten.

(e) *Dielectric heating*. When wet gluten is chopped into small pieces by the combination of an extruding machine and a fan blade, it can be dried down to about 30% moisture by the single pass of these pieces through a flash drier. The resulting gluten is dry on the outside but is still moist in the centre of the particles, and because of the case-hardening of the gluten pieces a grinding and re-drying process would normally have to be employed.

However, if this gluten at 30% moisture is fed on to a moving belt and passed between the plates of a dielectric heater, very efficient and explosive drying will take place with the resulting material being in a convenient form for grinding. The original wet gluten can be dried by this method but the large amounts of water vapour can be trouble-some. A forced draft, or vacuum conditions, must be used to get the moisture away and to maintain the efficiency of the drying operation. Again considerable bubbling and expansion of the gluten takes place, and this must be allowed for in the design of the plant. The degree of heat damage can be severe under some conditions.

Probably the use of dielectric heating can be more usefully employed in conjunction with a conventional flash drier in order to get the much greater throughput and to dispense with the recircula-tion and dry-mix grinding which is so troublesome in the normal drier.

Under these circumstances it is probable that in the dielectric heat-ing 1 kilowatt hour would drive off about 2 lb. of moisture. There-fore, considering 100 lb. of the case-hardened product contains 30% of moisture and that this is dried down to just below 10%

moisture, we have the 100 lb. of feed reducing to 77 lb. of final product, i.e. the water loss is 23 lb.

Thus the electrical consumption per lb. of finished material is about 0·15 unit.

Dielectric heating has been used in various industries for many years, and in particular in the wood and plastic industries. Essentially, it is only the theory of condensers being applied. The elementary condenser is made up of two plates of a conducting material separated by an insulating medium. The simplest type is that of two metal plates separated by air, which is the dielectric. In dielectric heating the condenser system is connected to a source of high potential, and to high-frequency oscillations. The material to be heated is placed between the plates. Because of the rapidly alternating system heat is generated in the dielectric as the condenser charges and discharges. Thus the material is dried from the inside to the outside and not, as in air-drying, from the outside to the inside.

WATER TEMPERATURE OF DOUGH WASHING

The effect of the water temperature in the dough-washing stage was shown in several pilot-plant experiments (15). A dough was prepared from a low-grade Manitoba flour having the analysis:

	% w/w	
Total protein	13·5	(soluble fraction 1·8%)
Moisture	15·3	
Remaining solubles	5·4	
Starch by difference	65·8	

The mix consisted of 84 lb. of flour with 5·4 gal. of water, and the dough was allowed to rest for 60 minutes. The mixer was a Baker Perkins ribbon-type machine, with the front blade revolving at 38 r.p.m. and the back blade at 64 r.p.m.

After the development time the mixer was filled with water at a controlled temperature, and after fastening on a lid, allowed to mix for 5 minutes. At the end of this time the machine was stopped and tipped over to pour away the starch slurry, but not the gluten, through an overflow. The mixer was then refilled with water at the same temperature and the procedure repeated. Six washes were necessary to obtain gluten at the normal 80% protein level (dried solids basis).

The results are shown in the following table and in the accompanying graph (Fig. 17). The figures are percentages of the total starch extracted.

Water temperature	1st Wash	2nd Wash	3rd Wash	4th Wash	5th Wash	6th Wash
10–15°C	18·7	26·4	23·1	14·2	8·8	8·8
15–20°C	17·7	29·4	29·4	16·5	5·8	1·2
20–25°C	23·7	34·4	25·8	11·8	3·2	1·1

The gluten in the 20–25°C experiment tended to break up into small aggregates.

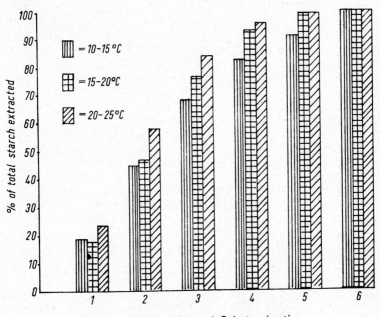

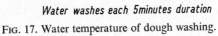

FIG. 17. Water temperature of dough washing.

WHEAT STARCH AND ITS FORMS

AFTER the extraction of the starch from wheat flour it is either used in the raw state or further processed into many different forms. These special starches all have particular properties which are required for one use or another in widely varying industries.

After an initial discussion of the properties and uses of raw wheat starch, several of the processed types will be described.

RAW STARCH

The manufactured starch is white and pure, having a moisture content of about 12%, and 0·2% of protein. When the starch is squeezed between the fingers a decided 'crunch' can be heard as the granules grind against each other. Wheat starch is unusual in that the size of the individual granules varies widely, the smallest being about 2 μ, while the largest can measure 35 μ (Fig. 18). There are few granules in the intermediate range. This contrasts with maize starch which contains a large proportion of the granules about 15 μ and which has a higher degree of uniformity. Again, potato starch has mainly large granules but varies from 15 μ to 100 μ.

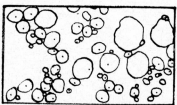

Wheat starch

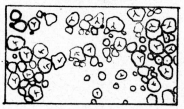

Maize starch

Potato starch

FIG. 18. Starch granules.

If a sample of extracted wheat starch is examined and compared with the starch still in the original flour, it can be seen that there are less small granules in the extracted sample. This is because the larger granules are more easily washed out during the

A) Dextrose crystallisers.

B) Section of a small H.V.P. plant.

PLATE FIVE

extraction process and a higher proportion of small granules are retained in the gluten.

Wheat starch is insoluble in water, but changes take place when the mixture is heated. When the temperature reaches 50°C the larger granules begin to swell, owing to the penetration of water through the weakened starch structure. At a higher temperature the smaller granules begin to swell also, although some of the smallest are very resistant to enlargement. At 65°C gelatinisation or pasting begins and proceeds rapidly and at about 70°C much of the granular form has become indistinct. During this process the viscosity of the starch/ water mixture increases and the thin slurry becomes a thick, semi-opaque paste. During this final phase the viscosity is high because of the crowding effect of the swollen granules, or more exactly, because of the hydrodynamic force of the balloon-like granules in aqueous suspension.

If this cooked starch is now subjected to high mechanical shear,

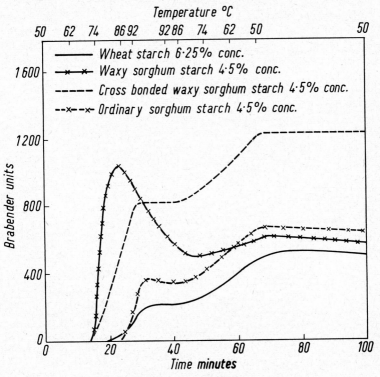

Fig. 19. Pasting curve for wheat starch.

41

the thick paste thins and becomes quite mobile. This is due to the disintegration of the structure into fragments which are no longer elastic. Wheat starch pastes are not as susceptible as some other starches in this respect, although all starches are thinned if the energy expended is at a high enough level.

If a cooked wheat starch paste is left to cool and to stand around for some time, the soft texture changes to a rigid gel and in time develops free liquid (syneresis or weeping). This is due to the chemical structure of the starch and will be explained later.

The Brabender pasting curve for wheat starch is shown in Fig. 19. This is obtained on the amylograph and is a convenient method for following the pasting history of a starch in water. A curve is traced for the rise and fall of viscosity with time and temperature. The suspension of starch in water is stirred by rotation of the container at constant speed together with the measuring device, which consists of short rods protruding into the starch mixture. The torque registered by the measuring rods is transmitted to a recording torsion balance. The temperature is raised at a constant and controlled rate up to and past the pasting temperature of the wheat starch. When the temperature has reached 92°C it is held at this point for 10 minutes, after

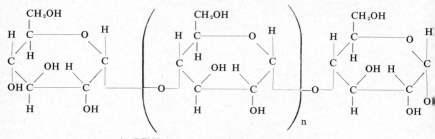

A. LINEAR or AMYLOSE FRACTION

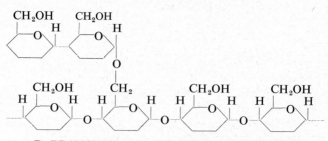

B. BRANCHED or AMYLOPECTIN FRACTION

Fig. 20. Amylose and amylopectin structures.

42

which controlled cooling takes place. A continuous and graphical record is traced by the instrument.

Like most of the common starches, wheat starch contains both linear and branched types of starch molecules. These two types, as shown in Fig 20, are (*a*) linear, unbranched chain of glucopyranoside (glucose) units, joined one to the other by 1—4 α-glucoside linkages, and (*b*) highly branched, laminated structure in which most of the glucopyranoside groups are joined as in the linear type, but at frequent points a glucopyranoside unit is joined in a 1—6 position.

In wheat starch there is present about 30% of the amylose fraction and 70% of the amylopectin fraction. Since the molecule is so high in hydroxyl groups, there is a great tendency for bonding between chains, and this is much more evident in the long molecular chain of the linear fraction than between the more complicated and shorter chains in the branched fraction. Referring back to the property of wheat pastes to form a gel, an insoluble precipitate, or to retrograde, this is due to the amylose content of the starch which gives this inter-molecular association to produce bundles of the linear molecules. This can be compared with waxy sorghum or waxy maize-starch pastes, which do not form gels at normal concentrations. They consist of the pure amylopectin fraction only and have no amylose to interfere.

The raw unmodified wheat starch is used in a variety of industries. To mention a few:

Food—Dried soups (usually low moisture starch). Baking powder, as an inert diluent. Canned foods and soups, as thickener. Coloured yellow and used as custard powder. Sauces, as thickener.

Paper—As a beater additive, either in the dry form, or as a slurry directly from the centrifugal separators in the basic separation.

Adhesive—For use on corrugated board machines as a slurry, cooked *in situ*.

Metals—As a sedimentation agent in the aluminium process.

Soap—Raw starch has been used in cake soap for a long time in parts of the world.

Laundry—As a laundry size for institutional use (usually mixed with borax).

Pharmaceutical—For tableting mixtures. Usually a low moisture starch.

Printing—As printing pastes.

Confectionery—Mixed with edible oil, and having low moisture for dusting purposes, e.g. jelly beans.

It has been found that by replacing 30% of the flour in an angel

c

cake formula with wheat starch, the volume of the finished cake is increased by about 10%. The grain and texture are also improved, and the product has a significantly longer shelf life.

Composition of Angel Food cake batter

	Normal %	Improved %
Wheat starch	0·0	4·4
Flour	14·5	10·1
Sugar	42·1	42·1
Egg whites	42·1	42·1
Salt	0·65	0·65
Cream of tartar	0·65	0·65
Vanilla to taste		

Wheat starch is also beneficial when used in pie pastry. Again, by replacing about one-third of the flour, better working and handling characteristics are obtained in the dough, the finished pastry looks better and is more flaky, and less shortening is required because of the reduced protein content.

It has been noted that wheat starch is used in biscuit making to increase spread and crispness.

CRYSTAL STARCH

The name of this product is somewhat misleading on a strictly theoretical basis, but it has been so known for many years and is, indeed, an old favourite for the domestic laundry. Using the top-quality starch, spun-dried but not heat-treated, it is slurried with a little water. Approximately 1% weight on the starch, of borax, is added, together with a blueing agent, e.g. ultramarine (this colouring for effect only). The thick slurry is now pressed into 6 in. or 12 in. cubes and wrapped in thick paper and kiln-dried at about 45°C for 14 days. When the blocks are removed they are gently broken up into the familiar nuggets of a hard, non-dusty nature. The cold water viscosity of these nuggets is very low and they slurry very readily. The product is an attractive household laundry starch.

PRE-COOKED STARCHES

For some purposes and in some industries, a cold-water pasting starch is required. This is a starch which has been cooked and dried and which, when mixed with cold water, forms a viscous paste. Although wheat starch is not particularly sensitive to temperature and time, as shown on the conventional pasting curve, under the conditions of drum pasting and drying a considerable proportion of the normal viscosity of wheat starch is lost and this shows up in the re-constituted paste. Moreover there is some retrogradation of the amylose content.

Pre-cooked starches are usually produced in two ways, by roller-drum drying or by spray drying. In the former the roller-drum equipment is either of the single or double variety.

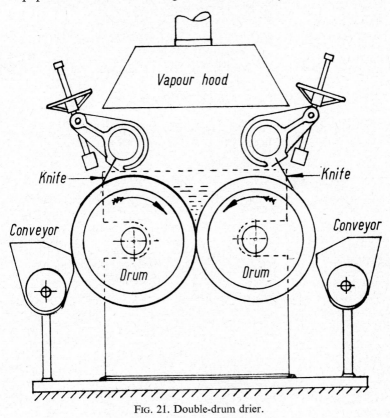

FIG. 21. Double-drum drier.

A typical atmospheric double-drum drier is shown in Fig. 21, and consists of two steam-heated drums rotating inwards towards the nip of the rolls. There is a reservoir of starch slurry contained and heated by the rolls. End-plates are fitted to prevent the starch being lost and to confine it between the drums. These plates, which are usually steel, must be faced with suitable material to ensure a close fit. The facing must have good wear and heat-resisting properties and could consist of bakelite, wood or fibre board, and should be replaced periodically. Leaking end-plates can be a source of trouble, affecting both quality and yield.

The reservoir of starch is heated to boiling point and some concentration takes place. Since the starch film adhering to the drum surfaces must pass through the small clearance between the drums, the liquid is evenly distributed. The clearance of the drums is adjustable and by this means the thickness of starch film is controlled. During operation the film must be removed at each revolution by the knife, efficiently, cleanly and in entirety, along the width of the drum. Any build-up on the surface of the drum can cause binding between the drums and result in damage to one or both of the drums. Again, the knives must not be under too great a tension, since this can result in scouring of the surface of the drum. The knives should be well maintained in a clean, sharp condition, and periodically removed for resharpening.

Obviously the best results would be obtained with drums which have a perfectly smooth surface, and in some factories it is the practice to run the drums for an initial period, and thereafter occasionally, on drying milk. This is said to fill in the imperfections or scars and to give a smooth working surface which is so desirable in the drying of wheat starch.

The starch slurry is usually fed into the nip of the rolls from a pipe, and the effect of the cold slurry can cause cooling on the drum rolls and produce a band of wet sticky material on the drums. This cooling effect can be avoided by having a narrow steel box, open at both ends, suspended in the centre of the starch reservoir. The cold slurry is fed into this and the cold liquor is prevented from spreading to the drum surfaces and is heated in the process of leaving the restraining structure.

The temperature of the drum surface is controlled by the steam pressure within the drums, and this must be varied from product to product. An efficient system of steam traps must be used in the steam supply line to ensure that water is not fed into the drum, and it must also be ensured that condensation is continually removed from the drum. A layer of liquid inside the drum can give completely misleading temperatures on the drum surfaces. The surface temperatures should be checked with a suitable pyrometer.

The rotational speed of the drums is adjusted until the starch film is just dry before reaching the knives. There is no point in running the drums at too low a speed, since this results in efficiency loss. The vapour from the equipment must be effectively removed by a forced draught hood, but the movement of air must not be violent enough to cause cooling and loss of heating efficiency.

A) Carter-Simon moisture tester.

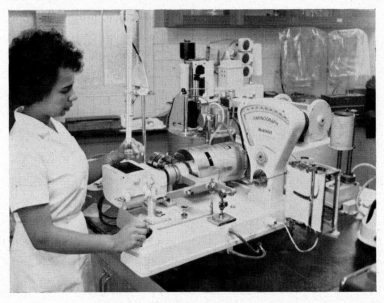

B) Brabender Farinograph.

PLATE SIX

The single-drum drier has some advantages over the double-drum machine and is probably more widely used. A typical arrangement is seen in Fig. 22. There are two feed rolls, a main and a secondary one, marked (A) and (B). The third roll (C) is a spreader roll. The (A) and (C) rolls rotate in spring-loaded bearings and are hard-adjustable. The main feed roller (A) rotates in the same direction as the main drum with its contact surface passing the drum in opposite directions.

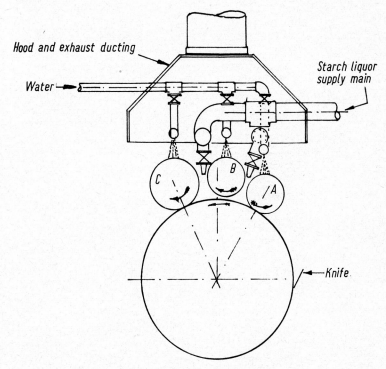

FIG. 22. Single-drum drier.

For most purposes in pre-cooking starch and starch mixtures, rolls (A), (B) and (C) are in contact with the main drum. The starch slurry of between 30% and 40% dry solids is fed by a travelling feed pipe into the space between (A) and (B). The moving feed traverses the width of the drum and back during one drum revolution. Roll (A) remains clean or has a very thin film, while roll (B) operates with a covering blanket of pasted starch. A sausage of pasted starch is maintained between (A) and (B), and especially between (B) and (C).

Under these conditions roll (C) becomes coated and the drum after (C) is coated with a double film. This gives a dense end product and high productivity. The sausage in the space between (B) and (C) is obtained from a secondary starch feed, or can be obtained by periodically or continually scraping a portion of the pasted starch from roll (B) to fall into the space between (B) and (C).

If a less dense material is required, then roll (C) can be raised, and the drier operated with only rolls (A) and (B). The feed is into (A) and (B) again, but there is only one sausage of material.

The single-drum drier has an advantage in being more accessible for maintenance than the double-drum variety. Other advantages are less wear on the drums, a shorter contact time for the cooking starch, less loss through damaged end-plates, a greater percentage of the drum drying surface is used, and a greater output is possible because the double-drum drier cannot imitate the double-film arrangement.

From both the types of drier the product usually comes off the drums as a continuous white film, and it is then conveyed away, ground and sieved. The final product can vary considerably in bulk density according to the film thickness on the drum. The thicker the film being dried, the higher the bulk density. It can also vary considerably in viscosity level. If the film on the drum is too thick, and sufficient water has not been present to allow maximum development of the starch paste, the viscosity of the end product is very low. In the author's experience some of the best pre-cooked starch, viscosity-wise, is produced on the double-drum drier with a feed of about 25% solids. It can be mentioned here that pre-cooked starch has lost the characteristic 'crunch' of the original wheat starch.

If the pre-cooked starch is intended for an edible product it is usually desirable to remove the 'wheaty' taste which is present. Under storage conditions this mild taste can become most prominent and objectionable. There are means to overcome or modify this unwanted flavour. In a patent (16) the use of trisodium phosphate to suppress the storage effects is described, while a process for the prevention of rancidity and starchy flavours in dry pre-cooked starches is claimed in another patent (17). The chemicals used in this treatment of the pre-cooked starches are described as sequestering agents, and are selected from the group consisting of tetrasodium pyrophosphate, disodium acid phosphate, sodium metaphosphate, sodium tripolyphosphate and ethylene-diamine-tetracetic acid (EDTA). It can be mentioned here that the production of good quality pre-cooked wheat starch is not such an easy operation as in the case of some other varieties of starch. The wide range in particle size means that invariably some of the smaller wheat starch granules are not effectively swollen and that the final starch is not fully pre-cooked. Physical separation of the large and small granules would undoubtedly improve the product.

For some purposes a small amount of wetting agent is added to the starch slurry before cooking on the rolls. This ensures thorough wetting and dispersion of the cooked powder in water before the starch is developed or swollen. When a pre-cooked powdered starch is mixed with water, an immediate swelling of the dried granules takes place, and lumps form. These lumps are difficult to disperse and it is preferable that some agent is present that will cause even wetting of the particles and some suppression of the rate of swelling. Some of the common detergents are useful in this respect, and borax has long been used in non-edible products. With the use of borax in the mixture the technique of drum-drying must be adjusted. The borax tends to form a 'glass' on the drum surface and the rate of drying is reduced. The use of too high a drum temperature will cause some fusing on the surface of the drum, which will give difficulty at the knives. Again there is a tendency for flakes, rather than for a continuous film, to be formed. These effects depend on the amount of borax present.

When pre-cooked starch is made for use in the paper industry as a beater additive it is essential that there is a definite suppression in the rate of swelling, since lumps of starch being formed at this point will cause 'fish eyes' or 'windows' in the finished paper. For this purpose soaps, vegetable oils and hydrogenated phenols can be used, but the use of various inorganic salts are preferred, such as hydroxides or silicates.

In the drum-drying of some pre-cooked food products containing starch, as for example cereal foods, the use of an α-amylase helps to improve the drying rate and thereby the throughput. Similarly the use of this enzyme for pre-cooked wheat starch can be useful. However, it must be remembered that the viscosity level of the starch is of much importance, and the amount of α-amylase added to the starch slurry must be carefully controlled. Sufficient must be used to allow the necessary breakdown of the starch structure to get the quicker drying without affecting the viscosity level to any large extent.

A good method of producing the pre-cooked starches is by means of a spray drier. The starch slurry is cooked batchwise in a stirred pot and then dried by spraying, usually under pressure, into a drying chamber. Alternatively a continuous cooker is used. Whether the method for pre-cooking is continuous or batchwise, the product can be precisely controlled, and exactly the amount of cooking at the desired temperature can be obtained. This is not always so in the drum-drying methods. A suitable continuous machine is manufactured by the Girdler Company of the U.S.A. and is sold under the name of Votator. This apparatus has been designed and built to give efficient heat transfer and to be rugged enough to handle very high starch-solid concentrations. In fact, it is claimed that as much as 45% starch in water can be handled. The machine is a jacketed cylinder containing a revolving mutator shaft which provides the necessary

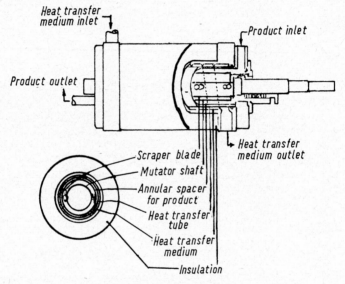

Heat transfer medium inlet

Product inlet

Product outlet

Heat transfer medium outlet

Scraper blade

Mutator shaft

Annular spacer for product

Heat transfer tube

Heat transfer medium

Insulation

FIG. 22A. Votator principle.

mixing of the starch to get an efficient heat transfer and which constantly moves the paste forward, cleaning the heat transfer surface continuously. The starch slurry is pumped under pressure into the apparatus and the cooked paste is then pumped straight to the drier. This gives a closed system, which prevents contamination and waste (*see* Fig. 22A). Incidentally this system can be used very successfully in conjunction with a drum drier as well as a spray drier. In this case the pumped cooked paste would be flashed before feeding on to the drying drums. With this system the drying capacity of the drums can be increased by about one quarter.

Roughly speaking, a spray drier consists of a closed chamber into which the feed is atomised by some device. A current of hot air meets the fine particles, conveys them and travels past them, vaporising the water. The dried particles are taken by the now moist air into some device, such as a cyclone, where they are deposited while the air continues on to an exit point (Fig. 23).

Under these conditions there is rapid evaporation of the water, and this keeps the temperature of the sprayed particles low. It is

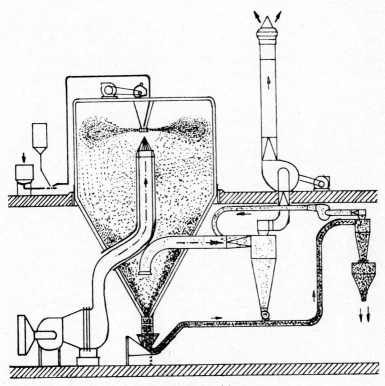

FIG. 23. Spray drier.

therefore possible to use fairly high temperatures in the drying air without over-heating the product.

The atomiser can be a rotating device in which the starch paste under pressure is fed on to a rapidly rotating disc and is thrown out horizontally by centrifugal force, breaking up into a spray as it leaves the edge of the disc. Alternatively a fixed spray device is used in which high pressures force the starch paste through a finely perforated head. In both cases the dried product is finely divided and consists of hollow spheres which re-absorb water very quickly because a larger surface area is present than in a normal solid particle. Without special additives this form of pre-cooked starch will lump badly when added back to water.

In any cost comparisons for producing pre-cooked starch by drum-drying or by separate cooking and then spray drying, it must not be forgotten that heat efficiency and actual cost of drying is only a small part of the overall considerations. The spray-drying method is one with good control; for no losses and no grinding process is required for the final finished product. On the other hand the material might be too powdery and might have too low a bulk density together with an undesired high rehydration rate. Both these types of processing have their advantages.

The pre-cooking of a starch by heat treatment and the subsequent drying of that starch is to produce a substance that will form a starch paste in cold or only warm water. The heat treatment has made the granule sac permeable to water, and it therefore swells. There are other ways in which this can be brought about. For example, certain chemicals cause starch to swell in cold water. Amongst others can be mentioned sodium or potassium hydroxides, potassium thio-cyanate and potassium iodide. There are many more.

When wheat starch or other types of starch are processed for long periods in a ball mill, or better still in a vibratory mill, they become cold-water-soluble, forming a starch paste of much reduced viscosity. The grinding has rendered the starch sac permeable.

With new and more powerful ultrasonic power machines being produced it is interesting to speculate upon their use in this direction. It seems possible that the starch sac can be attacked by ultrasonic energy at intensities as high as 500 watts per sq. in. and that maybe this treatment would render the starch cold-water-swelling without the severe disintegrating action that occurs in ball milling. If this were so, then one could produce cold-pasting starches, having a reasonable viscosity level, by mechanical methods.

USES OF PRE-COOKED STARCHES

In recent years the vogue of 'instant' foods and household products has become prominent and therefore the pre-cooked or instant starch has been used in increasing quantities. The most prominent of these foods has undoubtedly been the instant-pudding formulation. This enables the housewife to prepare rapidly a milk-based dessert without the need of any heat. A typical mixture consists of the following:

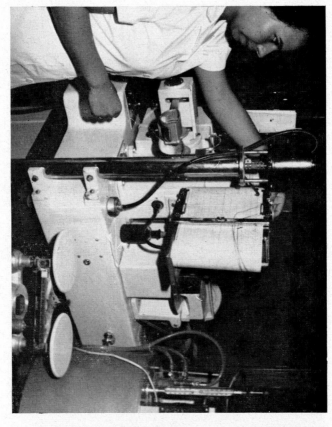

A) Brabender Extensograph.

PLATE SEVEN

B) Brabender Viscograph.

	% w/w	
Sugar	73·5	
Anhydrous tetrasodium pyrophosphate	1·7	
Anhydrous disodium phosphate	1·7	
Pre-cooked wheat starch	23·1	with various colouring and flavouring

or alternatively:

	% w/w
Hydrated (10H$_2$O) sodium pyrophosphate	2·5
Hydrated calcium acetate	2·0
Dextrose	20·0
Icing sugar	50·0
Pre-cooked wheat starch	25·5

About 90–100 gm. of the above mixtures are whipped into one Imperial pint of milk, using an egg beater or a cake mixer. After being beaten for about one minute, the mixture is poured into the serving dishes and allowed to set, a process which takes about five minutes.

The sodium pyrophosphate acts as a milk protein coagulant, while the disodium phosphate (or calcium acetate, which can also be used) acts as a coagulant accelerator. The pre-cooked starch is present to give stiffening and body to the finished pudding. It is obvious that the starch should not have a prominent wheaty taste and it must have been processed to eliminate this. Without the accelerator present the milk takes over an hour to set.

Another product that has been used in the home within recent years is the instant laundry starch. This is a starch that when sprinkled on to cold water will give a liquid suitable for starching dresses and table linen and the like. This eliminates the old practice of boiling a kettle of water and preparing a cooked starch paste. There are difficulties attached to the production of a pre-cooked starch which will do this job correctly. In the first place the starch must not lump when sprinkled into water. It must disperse easily and form a paste not too quickly and yet certainly not too slowly. It must be instant without lumping. Again, the paste when formed must be stable and not tend to thicken at the bottom of the container, since this causes heavy uneven deposition on a garment immersed for starching, and on a coloured cloth this becomes very obvious after ironing. The starch must not interfere with the colour of a fabric (e.g. opaque film), it must give 'slip' to the iron when being ironed and it must impart stiffness to the garment or cloth.

These requirements can be obtained in a pre-cooked wheat starch compound together with the use of various additives.

The modern do-it-yourself tendency has resulted in many people doing their own interior decorating, and this has provided a further outlet for a pre-cooked wheat starch as an instant wallpaper paste.

The use of a pre-cooked starch ether, rather than the straight starch, gives a very superior product.

Another domestic use of pre-cooked starch is limited, but interesting. This is the manufacture of the so-called 'finger paints' for young children. The pre-cooked starch, coloured with edible dyes, is easily mixed into a 'paint' with cold water, and this is used by young children for daubing. It does not matter if the 'paint' is eaten.

The first stage in the conventional papermaking process is called 'beating', the main purpose of which is to separate the pulp fibres so that they will felt together on the machine and form an even uniform sheet which has strength. At this point auxiliary materials are often added, and one of these is pre-cooked starch. Beater starch, as this is called, is often manufactured from potatoes, but in the parts of the world where potatoes are scarce or expensive wheat is sometimes used. The use of a pre-cooked starch in the beater stage gives a cementing action which binds the cellulose fibres together to produce papers with strength and several other desirable properties, equal to those obtained by high fibrillation by mechanical beating. This excessive fibrillation creates several problems in production which are not encountered by the use of starch.

The problem is to produce a pre-cooked wheat starch which is a white, free-flowing granular powder and which, when tipped rapidly, bag by bag, into the beaters, will disperse in the water and slowly form a paste. Again in this product the rate of hydration in the starch particle must not be rapid enough to cause aggregation before dispersion, because lumps formed here will produce 'fish eyes' or 'windows' in the finished paper. Also they can cause clogging of the felts, of the dandy roll and suction boxes, and sticking in the presses. A good laboratory test for the formation of lumps is now described:

Place a convenient volume of water in a beaker and tip sufficient of the powdered pre-cooked starch on to the surface to equal about 5% by weight. Give the mixture a few quick stirs with a stirring rod and leave for about 30 minutes. The paste should be quite homogeneous at this stage, and when tested with dilute iodine/potassium iodide solution should give an overall pale-blue coloration. No dark-blue spots should be detected.

The beater starch must also have a high retention value. That is to say, 75% or more should be retained in the finished paper. The reason for this is obvious from the economic point of view, but it is also very desirable from the operating point of view, since a high starch content in the filtrate or backwater can lead to slimes caused by micro-organisms.

These desirable properties in the pre-cooked starch are obtained by processing an alkaline starch slurry and using a thick film technique to obtain high density in the final product. Careful grinding and sieving, and the addition of the necessary slow pasting additive, gives the desired product.

One very important outlet for pre-cooked starch has been in the foundry field. Sand cores are made in moulds from sand and a binding agent. The moistened mixture is compressed and the wet core removed for a baking process. These formations are then used for the production of hollow castings, and the binding agent must possess several properties to be successful. It must give 'green' strength to the wet core so that it can be handled before being baked. Also it must confer 'dry' strength after baking and 'hot' strength during the pouring of the molten metal. It must not produce excessive gas during the pouring process and after, because this might weaken the casting by blow-hole formation, but at the same time it should burn away evenly, so that the sand is left in a state to be recovered after cooling.

A good 'cereal binder' for this purpose is made by pre-cooking a mixture of flour and wheat starch. The ratio is about 80 : 20 respectively, but can vary for individual customers. The starch should be the second-grade variety, being high in protein and pentosan content, since this imparts very high 'green' bond strength. The bulk density of the 'cereal binder' should be constant, because it is measured out in the foundry by volume and not by weight. A slightly borated mixture (up to 1% borax) produces a more stable binder, and the addition of sugar (in the form of molasses) helps to stabilise the product. The flour-starch mixture is cooked on the drums at a low steam pressure and the feed can be a thin dough. The rate of production is very high.

Pre-cooked starch is used in oil-well drilling muds in very large quantities, and the petroleum companies' large turnover has been responsible for the attention that some starch manufacturers have given to this application. The drilling mud is used in the drilling of holes and lubricates and cools the cutting-bit. It is circulated down the hollow drill and up through the hole, carrying the cuttings with it. The mud is essentially composed of clay with various additives. One of these additives is pre-cooked starch, which is added to improve the viscosity and water-retaining characteristics of the mud. This can be manufactured from wheat starch, preferably in a slightly alkaline state, and made under thin-film conditions to give the maximum viscosity. However, wheat starch has not proved to be the best of starches for this purpose, and it is particularly susceptible to breakdown in the presence of salt water.

In the preparation of various types of paper boards, raw starch is used as the adhesive. To take as an example corrugated board, this is made on a machine which corrugates a strip of paper, applies adhesive to the corrugations, and bonds them to a paper liner. This is the 'Single Facer'; the 'Double Facer' is prepared by putting on another liner on the reverse side in a similar manner.

The adhesive used on these machines is often prepared from a dry powdered mixture called *corrugating starch*, which is a mixture of raw wheat starch, pre-cooked wheat starch and borax. The proportions are about $84\frac{1}{2} : 15 : \frac{1}{2}$. The pre-cooked starch is called the *carrier* and is present to give the viscosity required in the aqueous mix to keep the raw starch in suspension. The raw starch is cooked by the heated rolls in the corrugating machine, and is the bonding substance. The aqueous mixture is made up with 2% caustic soda solution, and this is used to disperse the pre-cooked starch efficiently and to reduce the pasting temperature of the raw starch so that the raw granules will readily swell and burst at about 135°F.

Normal pre-cooked wheat starch with as high a viscosity as possible is used for this application. Thin-film formation on the pre-cooking drums will give this requirement. A similar formulation to the corrugating starch is used when moisture-resistant bonding is required. The waterproofing property is obtained by the addition of a phenol to the dry mix and the use of paraformaldehyde in the liquid mix.

Pre-cooked starches, including wheat, have been used as flocculating agents. Varying degrees of success have been obtained in the treatment of coal wash-water, uranium ores and the clarification of river water. A normal pre-cooked, neutral wheat starch has been used with inorganic phosphates as the admixture.

OXIDISED STARCH

Sodium hypochlorite is employed to oxidise wheat starch and thereby to modify several of its characteristic properties. As already mentioned, the linear fraction in wheat starch, the amylose, is responsible for the gel formation and the subsequent retrogradation after cooking. It has been found that by oxidising under mild conditions the linear chain is attacked at several points along its length and thereby loses some of its tendency to associate with other linear chains. The oxidised starch therefore has a lower rate of precipitation and has a clearer appearance than the original starch paste. The branched chain, or amylopectin, in the wheat starch is also attacked by the sodium hypochlorite, but this does not contribute much to the altered properties. The chemical attack on the starch also causes reduced ability for effective swelling by granule fragmentation and thereby the paste viscosity is lower, but the apparent dry granule structure is mainly unchanged and the starch is not cold-water pasting. Iodine gives the usual reaction.

The higher the degree of modification, the lower the viscosity or the higher the fluidity. This term fluidity refers to the volume of the cooked starch paste at a standardised concentration that will flow through an orifice of known dimensions in a fixed time. The thinner the paste the larger the volume flow in the time. The oxidised wheat starches are manufactured to various fluidity numbers and sold under these numbers. The general method used for this manufacture consists of preparing the wheat starch suspension in a suitably lined tank provided with some adequate means of stirring or circulation. The concentration of the starch slurry can then be adjusted so that the volume of water present can help in the dissipation of the heat produced by the exothermic reaction and thereby keep the temperature below about 32°C (90°F). The sodium hypochlorite solution is added and the pH adjusted until the starch slurry is definitely alkaline. The reaction is now left for about 5 hours, at which time an antichlor (sodium metabisulphite) is added, the pH readjusted to about 4, and the starch de-watered and washed. The filter cake is now dried and the pH will have come back to about 6 or 7. For producing a series of oxidised starches it is convenient to keep the reaction temperature, time, and pH constant, and to vary the amount of sodium hypochlorite.

The main uses of the oxidised wheat starches lie in the paper and the textile fields. In many cases the products are 'tailor-made' to suit individual mill conditions.

In the paper industry these starches are used as surface sizes and they have the following properties:

(1) *Viscosity* has been reduced to within the limits required to give penetration into the paper sheet, with the right degree of surface loading at the desired operating temperature and solids concentration.

(2) *The stability* is greater than in the parent starch and there is controlled retrogradation. It is not a good thing to eliminate completely the 'set-back' or retrogradation of the size. Such thixotropic set-back, if present in the right degree, will give a better degree of scuff-laying, produce a better pick figure and a more closed sheet without being sufficient to cause trouble through setting up (solidifying) in pipes or storage containers.

57

(3) *Low cold solubility*, contributing to high pick values and resistance to moisture in lithographic printing processes.

(4) *High protective colloid effect*, resulting in a finer dispersion of rosin size.

(5) *Good film-forming properties*.

(6) *Adhesive properties*, which assist in developing the film-forming and binding effect, have been related to the tack-development time.

(7) *Clarity, good colour*, no objectionable odour with near neutral pH, and absence of frothing.

Many of the above properties are desirable for the sizing and finishing of textiles as well as for the surface sizing of paper.

The basic purpose of warp sizing is to step up the efficiency of the weaving process. In general, cotton yarn is not strong enough to withstand the rigours of weaving and has many loose fibres, which because of entanglements cause breaking-out of ends. The protruding fibres also increase the friction between yarns and on parts of the loom. Sizing with an oxidised wheat starch stiffens the yarn by sticking the fibres together and there is a much-reduced breakage owing to the fibre slipping. The smoothing of the loose fibres on to the side of the yarn also permits easy progress through the loom and increases the abrasion resistance.

To get these effects and to avoid undue shedding, a degree of penetration of the starch into the yarn is required.

These properties are obtained by passing the yarn through a sizing bath of oxidised starch paste. The paste cooks without foaming in the cooker, has a good free flow in the pipes, and is easy to circulate at a constant fluidity.

Oxidised wheat starch is also used to prepare the liquid laundry starch which is now on sale in the stores and supermarkets. This is a product of convenience. It has only to be poured out of the bottle into water and mixed briefly with the hand, and it is then ready to be used for starching household items or clothes. To prepare this liquid product, oxidised starch of a convenient fluidity is added to water, together with a preservative, a dispersing agent and a dye, if the final product is to be coloured (usually blue). The starch-water mixture is stirred and heated to boiling, and thereafter maintained at a slightly lower temperature for about twenty minutes. At this time the starch paste is cooled to about 35°C and a solution of borax and sodium salts is added. Perfume and further preservatives are also added at this point.

The mixed paste is now homogenised for some time and then filled off into containers.

A) Protein estimations.

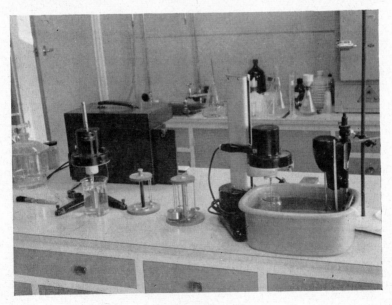

B) Brookfield Viscometer.

PLATE EIGHT

As an example:

Oxidised wheat starch	550 gm.
Water	5800 ml.
Sodium hexametaphosphate	10 gm.
Blue dye	0·1 gm.
Belloid compound	5 gm.

Heated to boiling with efficient stirring, maintained at 90°C for twenty minutes, then cooled to 35°C and the following added:

Borax	80 gm.
Sodium chloride	30 gm.
Sodium bicarbonate	30 gm.

These salts are dissolved in a little water and added, whereupon the paste is homogenised for fifteen minutes before filling into bottles. A mixture of 40 ml. of formaldehyde and 3 ml. of perfume is added five minutes before the finish of the homogenising period.

ACID-MODIFIED STARCH

In the same way that the oxidised starches are termed 'thin-boiling' because of their reduced hot paste viscosity, starches that have been treated with dilute acid at temperatures below their pasting temperature exhibit the same reduced viscosity and are also known as 'thin boilers'.

The main effect of the acid treatment is to modify the amylopectin fraction of the wheat starch. There is some fragmentation of the branched chain formation which increases the linear fraction of the starch and this makes it more possible for the pasted starch to retrograde into a gel. Although superficially the starch granule appears unchanged, when the starch is pasted the granule virtually falls to pieces to give a solution of low viscosity. These acid-modified starches are also identified by their fluidity number.

The method of manufacture is to introduce sufficient dilute hydrochloric acid into the starch slurry to bring the reaction mass to a concentration, acidwise, of N/5, and then to heat the mixture to about 55°C and to hold that temperature for several hours with stirring. When the desired fluidity is reached, the slurry is neutralised, washed, de-watered and dried.

There is also another method for making a type of acid-modified wheat starch. This is a 'dry' method, giving a 'mongrel' type of product, which is a dextrin type used as a thin boiler. The content of water-solubles in this starch is quite interesting, reaching as high as

10% in some grades and falling as low as 2% in others. The method of manufacture is to modify the commercially dry starch at a low temperature by adding a small proportion of mineral acid. A vacuum drier can be used for the modification.

Acid-modified wheat starch is mainly used in the confectionery industry, and a variety of gum sweets are produced by the use of this starch. It can be used mixed only with sugar, colour and flavour, or else it can be mixed with other colloids such as gelatin. The pronounced set-back of this modified starch makes it very useful for the confectionery industry.

The starch mixture is cooked and then poured into moulds. After setting, the gums are removed from the moulds and polished, or they are treated and given a sugar coating. The consistency of the finished gum can be varied by the degree of cooking which regulates the final moisture content. In some factories the cooking is done on continuous equipment.

Acid-modified starch is also used as a textile-sizing bath somewhat in the same manner as oxidised starch.

The flowsheet for a plant in which oxidised or acid-modified starches can be produced is shown in Fig. 23A.

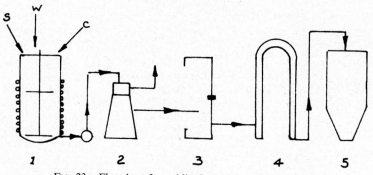

FIG. 23A. Flowsheet for oxidised or acid-modified starch.

(1) Jacketed reaction tank; (2) centrifugal separator (water wash); (3) starch de-watering centrifuge; (4) drier and grinder; (5) modified starch storage. S = Starch, W = Water, C = Chemicals.

STARCH ETHER

In Fig. 24, a representation of the starch molecule, it can be seen that on each glucose unit there are three hydroxyl groups.

As already discussed, these hydroxyl groups are responsible for some of the properties displayed by wheat starch. The hydrogen-

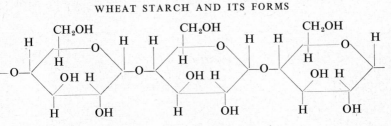

Fig. 24. Structure of starch molecule.

bonding property which causes attraction for other hydroxyl groups, for water, or for any other hydrophilic materials, results in the increased retrogradation of the pasted wheat starch. The tendency of the paste to thicken and then to weep, or for the dried paste to form an insoluble mass, is increased, because of the presence of the hydroxyl groups along the starch chains.

The chemical substitution in wheat starch at the hydroxyl group should therefore overcome the above properties, and indeed this is so. In fact the replacement of a relatively small proportion of hydroxyl groups by ether groups gives a product still in granular form, but which has markedly different properties. From the industrial point of view the ether, which is usually manufactured, is the hydroxy ethyl ether produced by the reaction with ethylene oxide.

The properties possessed by these starch ethers are listed:

(a) Reduced set-back tendency. This is due to the substitution at the hydroxyl group. Also this has the effect of reducing viscosity changes during cooling and ageing.

(b) Because of the reduced tendency for retrogradation, the paste is more stable to freezing treatment. The dried paste is also more easily re-wetted or redispersed in water, and is not insoluble.

(c) This starch ether has a lowered swelling temperature in water of from 10° to 20°C lower than the original wheat starch. Also the viscosity/time curve rises more steeply than the parent starch.

(d) The ether pastes tend to hold more water and are more cohesive, thick and long textured. This also means that there is less tendency for films of this material to penetrate into paper, and results in a more continuous film remaining on the surface. Because of the reduced tendency for retrogradation, these films are more transparent and more flexible.

(e) There is an increase in the response to borax which thickens the paste and also in the response to various synthetic resins which render the paste insoluble.

(f) The ether linkages are remarkably stable to acids and alkalis, and pH and water hardness are not so critical as with straight wheat starch.

(*g*) Good colour stability. Films do not tend to become discoloured under varying treatments.

The hydroxyl ethyl ether can be manufactured in a wide range of fluidities and with varying degrees of substitution. Wheat starch is acid-modified, as described in a previous section, to the desired fluidity, and the resulting slurry is then treated with sodium chloride and

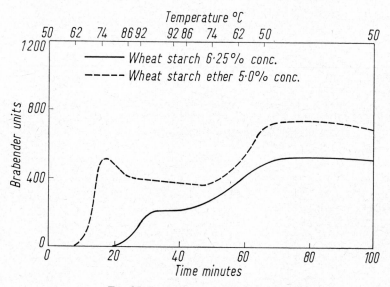

FIG. 25. Pasting curve for starch ether.

sodium hydroxide. The hydroxide is used to obtain the necessary high pH for the subsequent reaction with ethylene oxide, while the sodium chloride is present to prevent the swelling of the starch granules in the alkaline medium. The temperature of the reaction vessel is raised to about 50°C, and with efficient stirring the required weight of ethylene oxide is fed into the slurry at a constant, low rate. (The system has been flushed out with nitrogen previously.) The stirring is continued for about 20 hours, after which time the pH is adjusted to 6·5, and the starch is then washed, filtered and dried. For a successful reaction it is necessary for the parent starch to be substantially pure. Impurities, particularly protein, interfere with the substitution in the starch molecule and varying end products are obtained. The pasting-history curve of starch ether is shown in Fig. 25.

The hydroxyl ethyl ether of starch has not been passed as suitable for human consumption, and this prevents its use in a wide range of products in which its special properties would be very useful. Nevertheless, the ether is widely used in the industrial field.

One of the biggest users is the paper industry, and it is mainly employed here as a surface size. Because the ether has excellent water-holding and film-forming properties it is used extensively for improving the surface properties of a sheet and also for its strength characteristics. It can be used at the size tub or press and at the calenders, because of the wide range in fluidities and substitution values which are possible.

The films are resistant to greases and waxes and can sometimes be used in place of natural gums.

The flow, filming and ageing characteristics of the wheat starch ether makes it adaptable to a wide variety of general adhesive uses. In the single lining of board, as with glassine, a very good adhesive can be prepared from the ether with clay, sugar and sodium nitrate. The dextrinised ether products can be used for case glues, label glues and envelope adhesives.

The textile industry uses large amounts of the starch ether for warp sizing, finishing and printing of fabrics and the polishing and glazing of threads and cords.

A good household laundry liquid starch can be made by using a starch ether.

A good example consists of:

> Starch ether   7 parts approx.
> Water   77 parts approx.
> Borax   1·5 parts approx.
> Detergent   0·1 part approx.
> Preservative as desired
> Perfume and colour as desired

The mix is heated to about 90°C and held there for 20 minutes. After cooling the paste can be bottled.

DIALDEHYDE STARCH

In recent years work carried out in the United States has led to a practical process for the production of dialdehyde starch (18). Hitherto the reaction, outlined in the scheme shown in Fig. 26, had been only of laboratory interest.

Today this compound is in commercial production from maize starch, and although the author has had no personal experience of

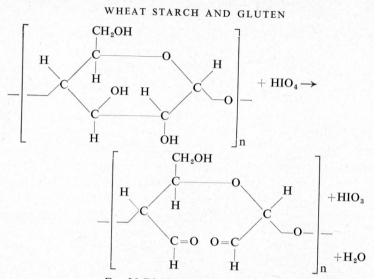

FIG. 26. Dialdehyde starch reaction.

the production from any other starch, there is no reason why the dialdehyde derivative cannot be produced from wheat starch. This further description of the maize product and its uses in this section can be applied to wheat starch equally as well.

The method of production is based on the original United States Department of Agriculture process (19), and is a combination of the electrolytic oxidation of iodic acid to periodic acid and of the chemical oxidation of starch to dialdehyde starch by the periodic acid. During the starch oxidation the periodic acid is reduced to iodic acid. The operations are all carried out in an electrolytic cell with iodic acid being oxidised at the anode and the periodic acid oxidising the starch in the anolyte.

Electrolysis is carried out for 48 hours or more for high oxidation levels, with octyl alcohol being used as a de-foamer. When the electrolysis is complete, the starch-anolyte mixture is filtered and the iodic acid removed from the starch cake by washing. The starch is then dried. The resulting dialdehyde starch is very similar in appearance to the original starch but has significantly different and interesting chemical properties. The following formula shows why this product is no longer a starch but rather a polymeric aldehyde.

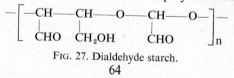

FIG. 27. Dialdehyde starch.

The presence of the aldehyde grouping means that many of the usual reactions associated with this group can be obtained.

(*a*) *Ammonia*

Dialdehyde starch and liquid ammonia (20)

or

Dialdehyde starch and aqueous ammonia in menthanol (21).

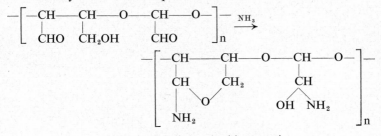

FIG. 28. Dialdehyde starch with ammonia.

(*b*) *Phenyl Hydrazine*

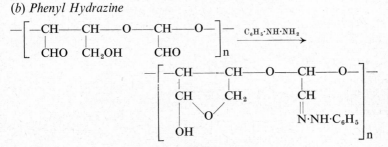

FIG. 29. Dialdehyde starch with phenyl hydrazine.
References (22) and (23)

(*c*) *Hydroxylamine*

By the usual methods.

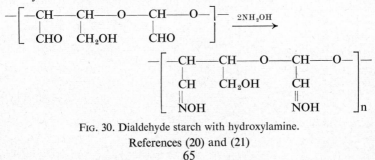

FIG. 30. Dialdehyde starch with hydroxylamine.
References (20) and (21)

(*d*) *Urea*

Aqueous slurry of dialdehyde starch + urea (20).

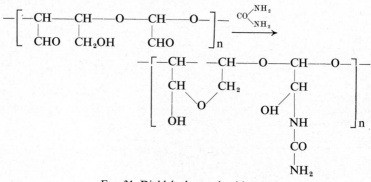

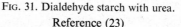

Fig. 31. Dialdehyde starch with urea.
Reference (23)

These reactions above are but a few of those described in the literature (*see* Refs. (24) to (31) inc.).

Although many uses have been suggested for dialdehyde starch, the main practical work seems to have been done in two fields, the paper industry and the tanning industry.

In the paper process, dialdehyde starch has been used as a beater additive and gives increased wet strength and dry tensile strength in the finished sheet.

In the tanning industry dialdehyde starch has been shown to have a tanning action, variable with the degree of oxidation. The most promising leathers have been obtained with the starch containing a high aldehyde content.

CATIONIC STARCH

There are indications that the introduction of a tertiary amino group into the starch molecule imparts a positive charge to the resulting compound. When this starch derivative is used with materials bearing a negative charge there is increased mutual affinity.

The compounds just described can be made by etherifying wheat starch with a reagent selected from the group of dialkylaminoalkyl epoxides, dialkylaminoalkyl halides or the corresponding compounds containing aryl groups instead of one of the alkyl groups. Examples of these reagents are β-diethylaminoethyl chloride, β-dimethylaminoisopropyl chloride, 3-dibutylamino-1,2-epoxypropane, 2-bromo-5-diethylaminopentane hydrobromide, N-(2, 3-epoxypropyl)-N-methylaniline.

The reaction may be illustrated by the following equation:

$$\begin{array}{c} C_2H_5 \\ \diagdown \\ \diagup \\ C_2H_5 \end{array} N \cdot CH_2 \cdot CH_2 \cdot Cl + HO\text{---starch} \rightarrow \begin{array}{c} C_2H_5 \\ \diagdown \\ \diagup \\ C_2H_5 \end{array} N \cdot CH_2 \cdot CH_2 \cdot O \cdot starch$$

FIG. 32. Cationic starch reaction.

The method of manufacture is to prepare a starch slurry containing 30 parts of sodium chloride in 125 parts of water and 100 parts of wheat starch. This is well mixed, and 3 parts of sodium hydroxide are slowly added as a 10% aqueous solution. 2 parts of β-diethylaminoethyl chloride hydrochloride are dissolved in 25 parts of water and then added, and the mixture maintained at 50°C for 24 hours, with stirring. After this reaction time the pH is adjusted to about 3·5 with dilute hydrochloric acid, and the starch is well washed, de-watered and dried.

The resulting dry starch is white and cold-water insoluble, but possesses changed pasting properties. The cooked paste is clearer and has less tendency to retrograde. Much more resistance to the effects of low pH are exhibited. These starches also exhibit compatibility with phenol.

The main use of this cationic starch is as a paper beater additive. It shows an improved degree of retention by the cellulose fibres and is therefore much more efficient in use. The finished paper shows improved strength. However, the starch is not inexpensive.

The more recent indications are that a starch will be preferred that is a combination of a cationic and a dialdehyde starch. Work is now going on in the U.S.A. with paper preparations containing added cationic dialdehyde starches to study their properties in the paper and to find the preferred compound. One possible route for making this type of starch is by oxidising the cationic compounds described above. The residues of the unsubstituted anhydroglucose are also oxidised, of course. Another way is to add the tertiary amine grouping to dialdehyde starch.

In order to achieve high wet strength in paper and improve the dry strength, high retention on the cellulose fibres is required. Latterly the use of dialdehyde starch in the paper industry has been by physical admixture with a cationic starch. A starch containing both the tertiary amine groups and the dialdehyde groups in the one molecular chain should be a most interesting material.

TORREFACTION DEXTRINES

When dry starch is treated with heat, alone or in the presence of a catalyst, a large number of degradation products are produced. The linear formation of the starch is split by pyrolytic and hydrolytic reactions and the resulting product consists of chain fragments of varying sizes. There is some evidence that recombination takes place among reactive chain fragments and a highly branched structure finally emerges with the resulting dextrines, as they are termed, highly soluble and stable. The process is essentially a combined one of pyrolysis and hydrolysis, and the end product is termed a torrefaction dextrine, no matter what stage the reaction is arrested at. When the reaction is carried out in the absence of a catalyst or in the presence of very small quantities of catalyst, the material has a secondary title and is referred to as a British gum. Pyrolytic reactions play an important part in the production of this product.

As in some other industries, the practice of producing dextrines from starch has been carried out for a long time, and often by rule of thumb, each operator having his own special technique and each product being different from the other. In fact the production has been an art and certainly not a science. With more knowledge about the reaction this attitude has somewhat disappeared.

A whole range of dextrines is manufactured, starting from those of a white colour, down through the creams, yellows, oranges and browns. Corresponding gradation of other properties are shown, with the paste viscosity being reduced rangewise, an increasing formation of cold-water solubles and a varying increase in the amount of reducing substances.

The method of manufacture can vary somewhat, but a general outline can be given. Wheat starch is taken from the primary separation process as the finished product in the dry, ground and sieved state. It has the normal moisture content of about 12%. At this point the acid is introduced, and this is usually hydrochloric acid or nitric acid in concentrated aqueous solution. The strength of the acid solution depends on the quantity of acid required and whether this volume requires diluting with water to give a sufficient volume for efficient dispersion. The smaller the volume of acid required the more dilute is the spray mixture, since the purpose of the operation is to spread the acid completely throughout the starch. This operation is an important one, and inefficient mixing of the starch and acid will result in local acid concentrations and black specks in the final product. The acid is often sprayed on to the starch, which is continually mixed or recirculated. Preferably, but difficult to arrange, the acid can be added to the starch slurry defore it is be-watered in the primary separation process.

After this step the acidified starch is dried down to a low moisture level, 6% in the case of the white dextrines and 4% or lower in the case of the coloured dextrines. This step is considered essential by most manufacturers although it is sometimes omitted. The drying can be done continuously in a ring drier, or batchwise in a jacketed agitator. The dried, acidified starch is now ready for the dextrinisation process. This is done in a fluidiser type of reactor or in an agitated, jacketed iron kettle.

The fluidiser reactor is a cone-shaped vessel fitted with a stirrer and heating coils or steam jacket. The fluidising is done with air which is passed up from the apex of the cone. The air is sometimes supplied through fine air-bricks and can be cold or pre-heated. The effect of the fluidising action is to make the starch behave like a liquid and flow. Some variations of this equipment are covered by patents (32).

The iron kettle type of dextriniser has been used for many years. It must be heated uniformly and designed so that local overheating is reduced to a minimum. Circulated oil heating in the jacket has some advantages over steam heating.

Although there have been attempts to produce continuous dextrine processes, the batchwise approach still has advantages over a continuous production. Even in the best-run plants there are always some variations in the properties of the finished dextrines, and if the production is in batches these can be adjusted one way or the other before the batches are dropped to the coolers.

The course of the reaction is followed by the properties mentioned before:

(a) Reduction of paste viscosity.
(b) Increase in water solubles.
(c) Colour changes.
(d) Amounts of reducing substances.

The rate and course of the modification is influenced by the temperature, time, acid concentration and initial moisture.

The process is continued until the required properties are obtained when the reaction is stopped by cooling in situ, or by dropping the batch to a cooling vessel. The fluidiser can serve as a reactor and cooler by control of the heating coils and by control of the temperature of the fluidising air.

At this point the batch is treated either by the adjustment of pH or else it is left in the acid state. Dry lime is added to, or gaseous ammonia blown into, the dextrine to adjust the pH. When the product is neutralised at this point it is more stable during storage, and this is the preferred practice. However, many types of dextrines are sold and used in the acid state, and manufacturers obviously prefer this procedure because it results in lower processing costs.

After this the batches are fed into large blending drums so that the batch variations, which do occur, can be evened out. At this stage re-moistening can take place if desired, and the finished dextrine brought up to about 12% water content. Re-moistened dextrines disperse more easily in water than low-moisture dextrines. Any black specks or discoloured particles should be removed by sieving. It should be mentioned that severe explosions can and have occurred in dextrine plants and all precautions should be taken to avoid the presence of fine dust in the atmosphere. Dry starch dust is a real and continual explosion and fire hazard.

Another method of making dextrines in a fluidiser which works very well is as follows: The normal wheat starch of 12% moisture content is dried down to 4% moisture content and then fed into a fluidiser. Dry hydrogen chloride is fed in with the fluidising air while the heating is taking place. In this way intimate mixing takes place and a good-quality dextrine results.

The finished products have cold-water solubilities ranging from about 2% to 99% and dextrose equivalents from about 1% to 8%. Some of the properties from the unmodified wheat starch persist through into the low-modification white dextrines, and retrogradation is still apparent in the pastes, which are, however, much lower in viscosity. In the more coloured dextrines this retrogradation tendency is very much reduced and they can be prepared as stable fluid syrups. These syrups possess excellent adhesive properties because of their polymeric nature.

Some of the highly soluble coloured dextrines are manufactured to retain a degree of set-back.

The main use of the dextrines is for adhesive purposes, and several types of adhesives are prepared.

(a) Liquid adhesive, which consists of dextrine, water, caustic soda and borax, together with a wetting agent. The liquid mix is prepared at the dextrine factory and is sold in drums to be cooked up as required at the point of application.

(b) Dry mix, which is mixed with water and cooked as required. This is much the same as the liquid mix but avoids the transportation of water, which is costly. This is a mixture of dextrine, borax, soda ash and various chemicals.

(c) Cold-water soluble mix. This is the above dry mix, actually made up and pre-cooked on drum rolls. The product is ground and sieved and then only requires to be stirred into water. This is a very popular product, since it requires no processing at the point of usage.

By far the most popular modifying agent for dextrines in solution is borax. This chemical gives a marked increase in the paste viscosity

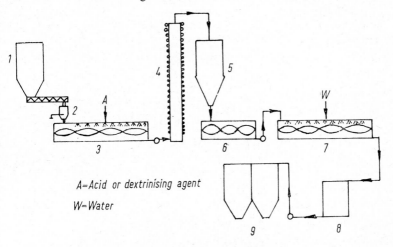

A=Acid or dextrinising agent

W=Water

FIG. 32A. Flowsheet for a dextrine plant.

(1) Starch storage; (2) starch weigher; (3) acidifier; (4) pre-drier; (5) dextrine fluidiser; (6) cooler; (7) re-moistener and blender; (8) sieving equipment; (9) dextrine storage.

and is even more effective in the presence of caustic soda. Fig. 32A shows a flowsheet for a dextrine plant.

ENZYMIC DEXTRINES

When a wheat starch slurry containing a small proportion of bacterial amylase, or a mixture of α- and β-amylase, is heated to its pasting temperature, liquefaction will occur within a few minutes. This is followed by rapid conversion to soluble starch and then to dextrines and sugars. A pH of about 6·5 and a temperature of 70°C are suitable with a time of about 4 hours. The resulting solution remains quite liquid when cooled.

The initial wheat starch must first be cooked at its pasting tempera-ture, since these enzymes are incapable of attacking the unswollen starch granule at any significant rate. The actions of the α- and β-enzymes are destroyed by boiling for about 20 minutes.

The resulting liquid can now be mixed with caustic soda or borax and dried by roller-drum drying or by spray drying. The dried compound is employed as an adhesive.

Some papermakers are using an economical method of coating their paper. They buy-in the raw starch, either in the dry state or as a slurry, and after adding an α-amylase they convert the starch by heating. The end point is determined by viscosity measurements and dextrose equivalent. The resulting dextrine is then used directly on to the surface of the paper. This method is cheap but open to trouble because of variations in the end product which can quickly arise.

GLUCOSE AND DEXTROSE

Having just previously described the production of dextrines from wheat starch by catalysed hydrolysis, it is but a simple step to arrive at the complete break-up of the starch structure into the basic glucose units by the same type of reaction.

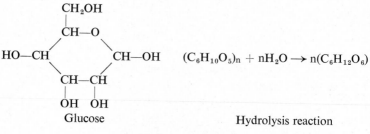

$$(C_6H_{10}O_5)_n + nH_2O \rightarrow n(C_6H_{12}O_6)$$

Glucose   Hydrolysis reaction

FIG. 33. Glucose reaction.

This reaction has been investigated as long ago as 1881 by Kirchhoff. The starch for this purpose should be as pure as possible, since the non-starch constituents form disagreeable taste and colour compounds under the influence of the acid treatment. Wheat starch is not one of the best starches for this production, because although a high-class product in good yield can be produced by the hydrolysis reaction, the presence of the pentosan and 'slimes' fraction in wheat starch makes the purification and filtration of the glucose liquors a more difficult task than in the case of, for example, sorghum starch. The fat content of wheat starch, however, is not higher than other common starches.

Some manufacturers go to great lengths to purify the starch as a pre-processing step, and enzymes are used which convert the insoluble protein into a soluble form which can be washed out.

In commercial practice the end product can take several forms and some of these are listed:

(*a*) Liquid glucose, which is a syrup.
(*b*) Sweet glucose, which is a syrup.
(*c*) Dextrose monohydrate, which is crystalline.
(*d*) Solid glucose.

Liquid Glucose

Liquid glucose is a conversion product in which the conversion has not proceeded to finality, but rather has been checked in an intermediate stage. Consequently liquid glucose is a mixture of the final product dextrose with various intermediate products, maltose and higher sugars.

The general outline of the method for the production of liquid glucose is now described. A water slurry of pure wheat starch at about 22°Bé (4·7 lb. of starch per Imperial gallon) is mixed with hydrochloric acid to bring the pH to 1·8–2·0, whereupon it is pumped into a copper converter. The conversion time varies with the steam pressure employed, and this usually varies from factory to factory between 30 lb. and 45 lb. per square inch (2 or 3 atmospheres). The course of the reaction can be followed by the D.E. (dextrose equivalent) determination (reducing sugars expressed as percentage of dextrose), and the coloration with iodine/potassium iodide. When the D.E. figure has reached about 45, the syrup is blown up into a neutralising tank, where sodium carbonate is added to neutralise the acid content. Carbon dioxide, water and salt are produced and the pH rises to about 4·5–5·0. The fat content of the syrup can now be removed in a centrifugal separator, after which the syrup is passed into a vacuum filter system. At this point the product is a thin aqueous liquid, but is not particularly free-filtering and may require the use of filter aid. The syrup is now treated with activated carbon and/or ion-exchange resins to purify it, resulting in a clear, colourless liquid which is then concentrated in some form of evaporator. After an initial concentration and a further pH adjustment the liquid is again clarified, and finally evaporated to about 43°Bé (containing about 80% solids). The resulting product is a viscous, clear white syrup which does not crystallise and which has a pleasant not-too-sweet taste. The properties of the syrup are illustrated by a typical set of results:

43°Bé, 42 D.E. Syrup
pH   5·2
Readily soluble in water
Hygroscopic
Viscosity[1]   40°C = 17,800 centipoises
                                    60°C = 2,800 centipoises
Moisture content   19·9%
Total solids   80·67%
Dextrose content   19·1% d.b.
Maltose   16·9% d.b.
Tri and tetra sugars   22·0% d.b.
Higher sugars   42·0% d.b.

[1] Fig. 34 shows the complete viscosity curve.

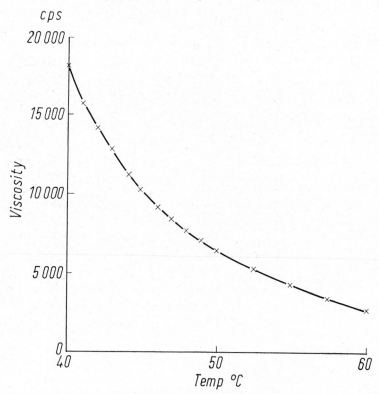

FIG. 34. Glucose viscosity curve.

Liquid glucose is used to a large extent in the confectionery trade, and particularly in the production of sweets or candies. The syrup is used specifically to:

(*a*) Prevent the crystallisation of sugar from causing graining.

74

(b) Retain moisture in the sweet. Products made with sugar alone dry out quickly, and glucose, being hygroscopic, retains the moisture.

(c) Add bulk and chewiness.

(d) Provide a nutritious product with reduced sweetness.

Other industries use glucose in varying amounts. Among the products containing glucose can be included: bread, pastry, beer, soft drinks, canned foods, glacé fruits, toppings, ice-cream, jams, jellies, pickles, sauces, leather tanning agents, adhesives and tobacco.

High D.E. Glucose

This type of glucose is prepared by an enzyme modified-acid process. Liquid glucose is prepared as described above, and after the purification stage the thin liquor (at D.E. of about 40) is treated with a fungal amylase. When the enzymic conversion has been completed in 24–48 hours, depending on the amount of enzyme added, the normal filtration-evaporation sequence is followed, finishing with a clear, white, sparkling syrup of just over 82% solids content. The action of the amylase is to extend the conversion to a higher degree and to produce a final syrup that is richer in dextrose and maltose. Consequently the syrup is definitely sweeter. Also this glucose is less viscous, has less tendency to crystallisation and possesses none of the bitter flavours sometimes encountered in the all-acid converted syrups in excess of 60% D.E. It is indeed a very attractive product, with a D.E. figure of as high as 65%.

A typical composition is shown:

43° Baumé, 65 D.E. Syrup	
pH	5·1
Moisture content	17·9%
Total solids	82·1%
Dextrose content	41·3% d.b.
Maltose	28·8% d.b.
High sugars	29·9% d.b.

Sweet glucose is used in a variety of foods and confectionery, in much the same way as is liquid glucose.

Dextrose Monohydrate

Unlike the glucoses this is the product of final and complete hydrolysis, and the crystallisation of that product, dextrose, with one molecule of water. There are two distinct methods for dextrose manufacture, one traditional and one of fairly recent development.

(a) *Acid process.* This is the older method and follows the familiar lines of the glucose process. A wheat starch slurry of about 12°Bé (2·4 lb. per Imperial gallon) is adjusted to a pH of 1·5 with hydrochloric acid and pumped into the converter. Steam is injected until a pressure of 45 lb. per square inch (3 atmospheres) is obtained and the reaction is taken to completion. This point can be determined by testing a sample of the reacted liquor with alcohol which causes any dextrine or starch to be precipitated. A further few minutes is then given whereupon the liquor is blown into the neutralising tank. A D.E. figure of about 91 is the end point. Sodium carbonate is now added to bring back the pH to about 4·5, and the fat content is separated by a continuous centrifuge. The thin liquor is now filtered and purified and concentrated to about 30°Bé, after which a filtration is effected. Then the final evaporation takes the solid content up to about 74% or 40°Bé. This syrup is now ready for crystallisation in the crystallisers.

As in most processes involving crystallisation, several types of crystals can be formed. Three types of dextrose monohydrate have been reported. One type is long and needle-shaped, tending to grow in bunch-like aggregates which are very difficult to wash and purify. Another type of crystal is a single, fragile, fine needle which shatters easily and forms an impervious mat. The last type is a plate form, flat and hexagonal, and is the ideal form when grown under conditions to give uniformity in size.

The concentrated, purified syrup is pumped into the crystallisers, which are horizontal cylindrical tanks fitted with slow-moving spiral agitators and surrounded by water jackets. Between one-quarter and one-third of the previous batch of massecuite (mixture of crystals and mother liquor) is left in each of the crystallisers as the seeding medium for the next batch of syrup. The spiral agitators revolve very slowly, and after about 3–4 days the batch is ready to transfer to the spinners, where, under centrifugal action, the mother liquor is withdrawn and the crystals are given a wash with a minimum amount of pure water. The crystals are now dried in some type of pneumatic drier, sieved and bagged.

The mother liquor from the centrifuges undergoes a separate purification treatment and is then concentrated up to 74% dry solids and recrystallised. The formation of this second-crop sugar takes longer because of the increased content of impurities. The dextrose sugar is separated and dried and sold as second quality. The wash water from the first-crop crystals is added directly into the main converted syrup at the neutralising stage.

The mother liquor from the second-grade dextrose is made acid again to pH 1·5 with hydrochloric acid and undergoes the total conversion process again. This yields good quality dextrose.

The above scheme represents only one of several which are

employed for the treatment of the liquors after the separation of the main first crop of dextrose. The final mother liquor or hydrol is a by-product with limited uses.

(b) *Enzyme process*. This has come into general use only in recent times. For a long time it has been known that certain fungal amylases produce glucose from starch, but the commercial existence of enzymes of the amyloglucosidase type which convert starch specifically and completely to glucose is of short duration (33), (34), (35).

In contrast to the acid process, which produces dextrose and reversion products at relatively high temperature and under pressure, the enzymatic conversion is obtained under mild conditions and with simple equipment.

The wheat starch structure must be dextrinised or heat-processed before the amyloglucosidase will do its work efficiently, and this liquefaction of the starch slurry can be done by a short acid conversion or preferably by an α-amylase treatment. In the first case the wheat starch slurry (20°Bé) is acidified with hydrochloric acid and given a very short reaction time in the converter to obtain a D.E. value of about 17%. The pH is adjusted to 4·5 and the thinned starch is then ready for the amyloglucosidase stage.

Using an α-amylase method the procedure is to adjust the pH of a 20°Bé wheat-starch slurry to 5·5 with sodium hydroxide or hydrochloric acid, and add the necessary very small quantity of enzyme dispersed in water. The enzyme used can be one of several commercially available which is high in α-amylase activity, which causes the rapid liquefaction and dextrinisation of the starch. The starch slurry-enzyme mixture is heated step-wise to 85°C and agitated slowly at this temperature for about 45 minutes. After this the mixture is cooled to 60°C and the pH adjusted to about 4·5. At this point the starch is again ready for the amyloglucosidase treatment.

The amyloglucosidase enzyme is added suspended in water and the starch batch is held at 60°C, with stirring, for between three and four days. The D.E. value is followed throughout that time and a final value of about 94% is reached with the acid/enzyme process and about 96% with the enzyme/enzyme process.

The converted liquid is now freed from fat, filtered and purified. After concentration to 40°Bé (74% dry solids), the syrup is crystallised in much the same way as in the acid process. However, the time for crystallisation is much shorter, being about two days for the initial crop. The separated dextrose is very pure and in a higher yield than from the acid process. Also the final mother liquid or hydrol, after three crops of crystals, is a golden liquid which can be concentrated into an attractive food product.

All reducing sugars are subject to alkaline degradation, and to prevent this dextrose is usually kept slightly on the acid side. It is available in a pH range of about 4·0 to 5·5 and may contain some quantity of buffer salts, such as acetates, lactates or citrates. Fig. 35 shows the pH effect on the converting activity of the amyloglucosidase and Fig. 36 a typical conversion curve using amyloglucosidase under optimum conditions.

A flowsheet for a dextrose plant is shown in Fig. 36A.

Dextrose monohydrate is a fine, white, crystalline powder which is odourless and has a sweet taste not as pronounced as sucrose. It has a specific gravity of 1·544 and a melting point of 146°C. Unlike most of the starch products it is a pure chemical containing one molecule of water of crystallisation.

It is widely used in the confectionery trade and in the food trade. It is also used in several pharmaceutical proprietary lines. It is often preferred to cane sugar because of its reduced sweetness. There is a considerable usage of dextrose in the bread industry, where it is used because of its quickness and completeness in fermentation and also because it imparts a golden-brown colour to the crust and gives a longer keeping period to the loaf. The crust coloration is due to the Maillard reaction which is the combination of nitrogenous compounds with dextrose at elevated temperatures to produce brown compounds. This property also makes dextrose useful in the manufacture of caramel colour and caramelised flavour in many food products.

SOLID GLUCOSE

This product is also known as 'chip' or 'slab' sugar and is prepared from the converted and purified liquor in the dextrose monohydrate process, just prior to concentration and crystallisation. Either the acid or the enzyme process can be used. The liquor is taken and concentrated to a higher solids content than in the dextrose process, in fact to about 81% solids, and then cast into pans. The whole liquor solidifies and is left to mature for two weeks or more, after which it can be chipped up with revolving blades. The sugar product prepared in this way from the total enzyme process has an excellent white colour and contains about 94% dextrose (dry basis).

AMYLOSE AND AMYLOPECTIN SEPARATION

As already mentioned, wheat starch is a mixture of linear and branched molecules, referred to as amylose and amylopectin frac-

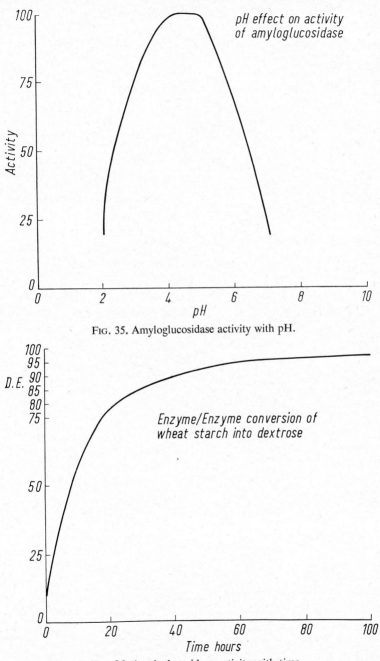

FIG. 35. Amyloglucosidase activity with pH.

FIG. 36. Amyloglucosidase activity with time.

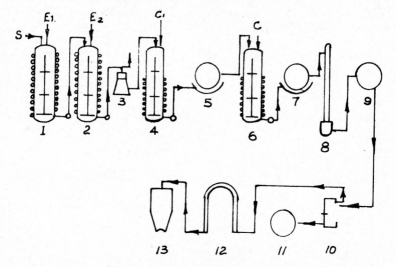

FIG. 36A. Flowsheet for a dextrose plant.

(1) Jacketed tank for starch liquefaction; (2) jacketed tank for amyloglucosidase stage; (3) centrifugal separator for fat; (4) jacketed tank for purification; (5) filter; (6) as (4); (7) as (5); (8) evaporator; (9) crystalliser for first crop; (10) de-watering centrifuge; (11) crystalliser for second crop after concentration; (12) drier and grinder; (13) storage for dextrose and bagging-off.

S = Starch slurry from separation process; E_1, E_2 = Enzymes; C = Activated charcoal; C_1 = Once-used activated charcoal.

tions. Several laboratory methods have been described for the separation of these fractions, but they are not adaptable to manufacturing processes. One such method described in several publications by Schoch (36) depends on heating starch in an aqueous, aliphatic alcoholic suspension under pressure. On slow cooling the amylose fraction can be separated by super-centrifuging. Further cooling gives the amylopectin starch.

In more recent times the separation has become a commercial reality. Work carried out in the Netherlands has resulted in a successful process and this is the subject of several patents (37). An example of the method is described with the starting material, de-fatted wheat starch. 5% by weight of starch is dissolved at 125°C under pressure in a solution containing 25 gm. of magnesium sulphate heptahydrate and 1 ml. of amyl alcohol per 100 ml. solution. It is heated for $2\frac{1}{2}$ hours, and on cooling to 90°C the amylose precipitates almost quantitatively in a form easily isolated. On further cooling to about 0°C the amylopectin separates out in good yield.

The separated fractions are dried and are cold-water soluble, having been cooked during the separation process.

An evaluation curve of the amylopectin fraction is shown in Fig. 37. The details of this test are given in the chapter headed 'Laboratory Methods'.

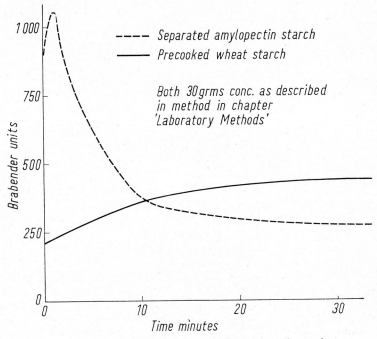

FIG. 37. Evaluation curve for separated amylopectin starch.

STARCH PHOSPHATES

In the U.S.A. and in Australia there are plants producing pure amylopectin starch from the natural sources of waxy maize and waxy sorghum grain. Some of this starch is sold in the unmodified form, but much is converted into a 'di-starch' phosphate form. By reacting the amylopectin starch with various phosphorus compounds (e.g. phosphorus oxychloride) a bridging or cross-bonding between starch granules is effected. This means that, upon cooking the modified amylopectin starch to a paste, the natural behaviour, which is high swelling of the starch granules giving a high viscosity and subsequent rapid solubilisation and breakdown in viscosity, is replaced by a different paste behaviour. The modified amylopectin shows no pasting peak and the granules do not disintegrate during further cooking, but are extremely stable. The texture of the paste is altered from long and stringy to short and soft.

The application of this cross-bonding process to ordinary wheat starch, which is a mixture of amylose and amylopectin, gives no startling or comparable effect. The mild conditions normally used in converting the waxy starches are not effective in the case of wheat starch.

Recently there has been developed a new class of starch phosphates (38). These substances are cold-water soluble, modified starches, possessing extraordinary thickening and stabilising properties in cold water. They may be described as being both hydrophilic colloids and anionic polyelectrolytes, and they differ from the usual drum-dried, cold-water dispersible starches. The normal pre-cooked starches have their granular structure destroyed, but these starch phosphates still retain the discrete granular structure of the original untreated starch. When they are dispersed in cold water the resulting pastes are semi-translucent, very thick-bodied, short-textured and display a lack of tendency to gel or set-back. This stability continues under cold storage conditions. The paste is brown in colour and possesses a toasted flavour. These last two properties are not particularly desirable for food products, but the toasted flavour is lost in dilution and blends well in many food items. The colour is more of a drawback, but a bleached product can be made. The ash content of the paste is high, being about 7% on a dry solids basis.

Acid and electrolytes reduce the viscosity of the paste by reducing the hydration of the polymer. Heat and/or mechanical shear reduce the viscosity by breaking up the granule, and stability here would not be comparable to the stability shown towards heat and shear by a modified amylopectin starch paste.

Basically the method of preparation is as follows:

The de-watered wheat-starch cake is blended with varying amounts of a neutral orthophosphate salt. The mixture is dried as the wet cake normally would be dried, and this is followed by a dextrinisation process. The dry roasting is carried to the point where cold-water solubility and thickening power in cold water reach a maximum. Contrary to the usual dextrinisation process, the starch phosphate compounds increase in thickening power rather than decrease during roasting. A colour develops during this stage.

The uses of these starch phosphates have not been fully explored, but it would seem possible that among industries who would be interested are the food, cosmetic, pharmaceutical, textile, paper and adhesives industries. A somewhat similar type of product can be produced by dry-mixing other types of phosphate salts with wheat starch, and roasting the mixture for various times and at various temperatures.

A viscosity curve is shown in Fig. 37A for two types of the starch

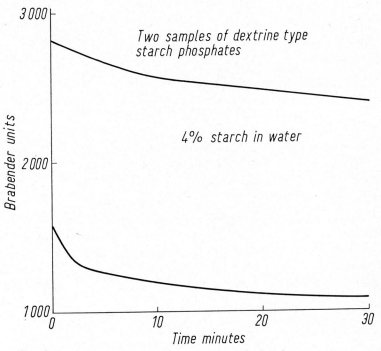

FIG. 37A. Evaluation curves for starch phosphates.

phosphates. The technique described in the chapter on Laboratory Methods could not be used because sucrose prevents the complete development of these starch phosphates. A straight mixture of starch and water was used.

3

GLUTEN

In 1745 it was recorded (39) that Beccari, Professor of Medicine in the Anatomy and Chemistry Institute of Bologna, Italy, had formed a dough from wheat flour, and by washing this with water had isolated gluten. This was the beginning of much literature to be published on gluten and the flour proteins.

COMPOSITION

The total proteins in flour have been roughly divided into two fractions, the soluble fraction and the insoluble fraction. The soluble portion is obtained by extracting flour or manipulating dough with water. A more complete extraction can be effected with sodium chloride solution. The insoluble fraction is known as gluten.

The soluble protein fraction is a complex mixture containing several globulins and an abundance of albumin substances. Globulins are protein compounds which are insoluble in water but soluble in dilute salt solutions. They constitute about 7% of the total flour protein. Albumins are proteins which are water-soluble. It seems quite evident from recent work that the albumins contribute to the baking performance of bread and that omission of the fraction from a bread dough causes inferior results. About 9% of the total flour protein is present in the albumin fraction.

The most important flour protein, and that which has received by far the most attention throughout the years, is the mixture (the insoluble fraction) called gluten. In the extraction process from flour, the crude impure gluten is isolated as a creamy-coloured, coherent, somewhat rubber-like, wet mass which has considerable extensibility. This impure wet gluten, containing about 65–70% of water, is then in its most active state, and although in commercial production the impure gluten is dried and finally ends up as a fine powder, the original wet-state properties are the criterion for the dried gluten.

The commercially produced, dried, crude, impure gluten contains 75–80% protein (N × 5·7). The non-protein portion is mainly 5–15% carbohydrates, which consists mainly of residual wheat starch. The remaining fraction of 5–15% is a mixture of fats of various types, otherwise known as lipids. The lipids appear to be combined with protein, for they are not extractable with ethyl or petroleum ether.

In this commercially produced gluten there is also incomplete removal of the so-called soluble proteins, and over 50% of the albumins and globulins remain in the gluten fraction. Sodium chloride solution can be used to produce a gluten free from the soluble proteins, but this will mean that the resulting gluten does not behave in a normal manner, being short and ragged, which gives poor results in baked goods.

A fraction of gluten dissolves in 60% aqueous alcohol, and for many years this has been known as gliadin. The remaining portion which is insoluble in neutral solvents but soluble in acidic or alkaline solvents is known as glutenin. These two terms are somewhat inaccurate because they do not designate absolute chemical substances but they have been retained for convenience (40). The physical properties of the wet gliadin and wet glutenin are quite revealing. Gliadin forms a soft and sticky mass which is very much like thick glue. Glutenin swells considerably and becomes tough and inextensible with no coherence.

Recently (41) gliadin has been divided into at least eight components, and glutenin is known to be a complex mixture.

STRUCTURE

The elasticity of gluten is attributed to the coiled and folded protein molecules (polypeptide chains), while the plastic flow can be explained as imperfect rigidity, due to slipping in the protein molecular arrangement. It has been proposed (42) that gluten forms a polyplatelet sheet structure during the hydration period and that these platelets consist of coiled polypeptide chains with their hydrophilic side-chains oriented outwards and their hydrophobic side-chains oriented inwards. There is also formed a small proportion of a lipoprotein complex which consists of two or more protein chains bound by phospholipid material present in the form of bimolecular leaflets. The linkage between the lipid and the protein is a salt-like bond between the acidic group of the phospholipid and the basic protein groups. These lipoprotein leaflets occur as random filling among the protein platelets and interfere with the orderly bonding between the protein platelets. Assuming that the bonding between the layers of the bimolecular phospholipid leaflets is weaker than the bonding between the protein platelets, there is provided a random weakness throughout the protein structure wherever the phospholipid filling occurs. Therefore an applied stress to the gluten structure will result in slip along the interfaces of phospholipid layers before the rupture strength of the interprotein bonds is reached. This gives the plastic-flow properties, so important in the gluten complex. It can be seen that too much of the lipid filling would result in a runny gluten, while too little would give a tough and short gluten. The importance of this proposed structure can be seen, and it takes little imagination to realise how easily and inevitably the 'vitality' of the gluten can be lost in the drying process.

The protein platelets are composed of coiled polypeptide chains, and the polypeptide chains are in turn built up from the individual amino-acids. The prototypic structure of an amino-acid is:

Fig. 38. Structure of an amino-acid.

and the various amino-acids are linked schematically through loss of water from α-carboxyl and α-amino groups giving a peptide linkage:

$$-CO \cdot NH \cdot CHR \cdot CO \cdot NH \cdot CHR' \cdot CO \cdot NH - CHR'' - CO -$$

Upon hydrolysis the polypeptide chain is broken, giving back the original amino-acids.

AMINO-ACIDS

The amino-acid content of gluten, as prepared commercially, is well known and it has been found that this composition is fairly constant, even though gluten from a wide variety of flours may be used.

The amino-acid composition is discussed later, in the section describing hydrolysed vegetable protein. The range of amino-acids obtained from wheat gluten is shown below:

Essential in Human Nutrition	Non-essential
Isoleucine	Alanine
Leucine	Arginine
Lysine	Aspartic acid
Methionine	Cystine
Phenylalanine	Glutamic acid
Threonine	Glycine
Tryptophane	Histidine
Valine	Proline
	Serine
	Tyrosine

From a nutritional point of view gluten is unbalanced in terms of essential amino-acids. Taking whole egg as the standard, gluten is sufficient in leucine, isoleucine, valine, methionine, phenylalanine, threonine and tryptophane, but low in lysine content.

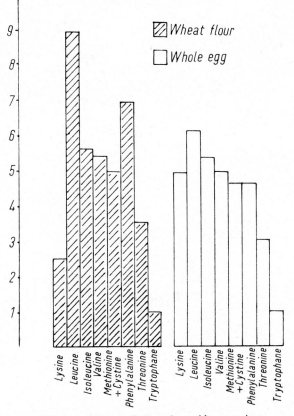

FIG. 39. Egg and wheat flour amino-acid comparison.

PROPERTIES

There are differences in the physical properties of gluten derived from different types of flour. The 'strength' of gluten varies considerably, and it has been suggested that the ratio of gliadin to glutenin is responsible; but it is now evident that this ratio variation is too small to account for the differences experienced.

The properties of gluten can be altered by the effects of various reagents. The use of certain oxidising and reducing agents is well known and it is common practice in flour mills to 'age' freshly produced flour which is under-oxidised. The effect of oxidising gluten is to toughen it up and to reduce the extensibility. Indeed, over-oxidation will cause the gluten to become ragged and brittle. Reducing agents will reverse the effect and cause great extensibility. The chemical groups involved in this reaction with oxidising and reducing agents are in the methionine, cysteine and cystine portion of the peptide chains.

Oxidising Agents	*Reducing Agents*
Potassium bromate	Sodium sulphite
Potassium iodate	Thioglycolic acid
Chlorine dioxide	Glutathione
Chlorine	
Ammonium persulphate	
Nitrogen trichloride	
Sodium chlorite	
Iodoacetic acid	

EFFECT OF HEAT

When gluten is exposed to heat treatment the main effect is to destroy some or all of the so-called 'vitality' of the gluten. This term has arisen from the use of gluten and gluten-in-flour in the preparation of bread. Gluten separated from flour, and used in the wet form, gives all the desired properties exhibited by the gluten as it exists in the flour. But when exposed to heat and drying treatment, the gluten loses some of its ability to produce a first-class loaf of bread. It is appropriate here to explain the role that gluten plays in the preparation of a loaf of bread.

The changes involved in the baking process are complex, and result in an unpalatable dough being transformed into a light, porous and appetising product. The first important change in the dough is a rapid expansion in volume due to the increased gas pressure within the dough. The increase in gas pressure is due to a rise in temperature, which apart from the purely physical effect, causes reduction of the amount of carbon dioxide dissolved in the dough liquor and also causes vaporisation of the low-boiling chemicals present. Again, the rate of gas generation by the yeast is increased with temperature until the thermal death-point is reached, about 65°C.

The starch granules also begin swelling, and in so doing take up water from the other ingredients. The hydrated gluten, being present throughout the entire dough, has expanded with and has supported it. It has provided an intricate cellular framework, allowing the minute gas cells to expand, but is extensible and strong enough to maintain the cellular form. The gluten forms the structural support for the dough piece until the starch can assume this role, after it has become hydrated and fully swollen. At this point the gluten loses water to the starch and tends to become soft with the increasing temperature. Finally, protein coagulation sets in, and the role of the gluten in the baking process is diminished.

The properties for a successful gluten are, therefore, a high degree of hydration, a good degree of extensibility with an associated strength and a light colour. The loss of 'vitality' means poor hydration, a shortness rather than an extensibility, and loss of strength.

The effect of heat on gluten varies according to the moisture content of the gluten. With moisture content of less than 15% the rate of denaturation at temperatures up to 100°C is quite small. However, as the moisture content rises, the heat damage rate is greater, until a peak is reached at about 40% moisture. Thereafter, with increasing moisture, the rate of denaturation becomes smaller again.

Under mild alkaline conditions gluten loses its 'vitality' much more quickly when heated than under mild acid conditions. Strong alkaline or strong acid will cause damage to gluten without any heating taking place.

The effects of time, temperature, moisture content, pH and salt concentration on the denaturation of gluten by heat have been studied by Pence, Mohammad and Mecham (43).

USES OF GLUTEN

Vital gluten is used extensively as an ingredient in yeast-raised baked goods, particularly bread. The preferred form of the gluten is in its hydrated, freshly extracted form, which has not been subjected to any of the degrading effects of drying. However, a lot of gluten is used in the dried form, and some very fine, carefully dried powders give results in bread very nearly as good as the original wet substance.

The obvious effect of introducing gluten into a bread mix is to increase the final protein content of the finished loaf. This in itself is an attractive feature, and in these days of diet fads much is made of protein-enriched or starch-reduced bread. However, the use of added gluten does much more for a loaf of bread than merely to enrich the protein content.

Taking as an example a baker's flour of 11% protein 'as is' with good baking characteristics, the scores recorded in a test kitchen are shown when unenriched loaves were baked from this flour and compared with loaves baked from other samples of similar flours.

2-hour Dough 1 lb. Tin Loaves	
Loaf volume: 1950 ml. (Max. score 36)	36
Loaf appearance (Max. score 20)	18
Crumb texture and grain (Max. score 30)	27
Crumb colour (Max. score 14)	14
Total (Max. 100)	95

The score of 95 indicates that in its own class this flour gave a good loaf of bread.

Now when 18 lb. of wet gluten or 6·5 lb. of dry gluten are added to each 140 lb. of the flour, the result is a flour containing 15·4% protein on a dry-solids basis. When baking tests were done on these enriched flours the resulting scores are most enlightening.

2-hour Dough 1 lb. Tin Loaves	Baker's Flour— Control with No Added Gluten	Baker's Flour— with Added Dry Gluten	Baker's Flour— with Added Wet Gluten
Loaf volume (Max. score 36)	1,950 ml. 20	2,200 ml. 30	2,325 ml. 36
Loaf appearance (Max. score 20)	16	16	18
Crumb texture and grain (Max. score 30)	24	25	27
Crumb colour (Max. score 14)	13	12	13
Total (Max. 100)	73	83	94

From this can be seen the effect of the added gluten (44). A much greater volume of loaf with better crumb texture is obtained. Particularly is this so in the case of wet gluten. Moreover, the dough yields are increased because there is a greater absorption of water, and the finished loaf has a longer shelf life because of the finer grain and softer texture. The total score of 83 for dry gluten and 94 for wet gluten indicates the difference in performance between the commercially available materials. However, it has now been demonstrated, both in the laboratory or test kitchen, and in commercial bakeries (45), that dry gluten can be prepared in a form which will give a performance in bread equal to that of wet gluten. Diminution of the gluten to a very fine state raises the baking score of 83 to between 94–96 and gives more tolerance in use.

The usefulness and effectiveness of wet or dry gluten in upgrading the performance of a flour can be demonstrated in the Brabender Farinograph. The enriched flour containing sufficient gluten to raise the protein content to about 15% (dry-solids basis) is tested in the

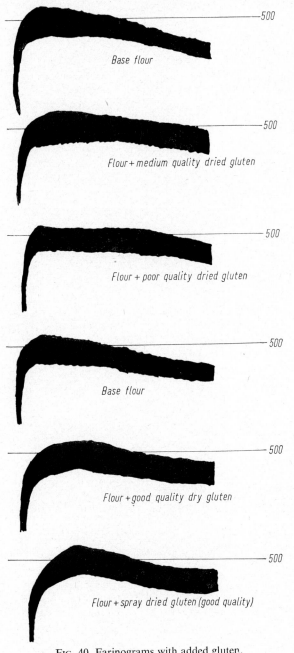

FIG. 40. Farinograms with added gluten.

usual way (*see* appropriate chapter), and the resulting farinogram compared with one drawn from the unenriched flour. Examples are shown in Fig. 40.

Gluten can be used in macaroni products to give an improved resistance to breakage in the extruded dried product. Taking a sample of spaghetti at 10·8% protein and one raised to 12·7% protein by the addition of a good sample of 'vital' gluten, the breaking strength is increased by 10%.

Much the same result is obtained in pretzels, and the breakage can be reduced by adding about 1% of gluten by weight of the flour. Indeed, if too much gluten is added to the pretzel mixture, they become too hard to eat.

Another use to which gluten has been put is as an adhesive. If wet gluten is mixed with acetic acid and then left in a warm room for several days, it will thin and liquefy. The enzymic action completely destroys the natural structure of the gluten, and the acetic acid prevents any putrefaction. When this thin liquid is dried, a brown substance is obtained which makes a very good glue when mixed with water. Shoemakers have been known to use this.

Gliadin, which is obtained from gluten by alcohol extraction, has been shown to be useful in textile dry-cleaning by preventing soil deposition (46). Gliadin is also useful as a whipping and foaming agent (47). In this respect whole gluten can be treated to give useful whipping properties. Wet gluten is treated with a powerful protease, and the resulting liquid can be dried in several ways to give a bland-tasting, light-coloured powder. This exhibits foaming and whipping properties. This product is also valuable for pharmaceutical preparations containing high protein values. The typical gluten 'vitality' has been completely destroyed.

GLUTEN SULPHATE

When wheat gluten is treated with sulphuric acid or a chlor-sulphonic acid-pyridine reagent, the resulting product is a non-hygroscopic, light-brown coloured powder. This powder has the remarkable property of absorbing many times its weight of water to form a pale transparent gel. Although this substance was described some years ago (48), and although it possesses very interesting properties, little or no commercial use has been made of it. No doubt this is mainly due to the costly manufacturing procedure.

Chlorosulphonic Acid Process

The sulphating reagent is prepared by adding 10 mols. (666 ml.) of chlorosulphonic acid to 47 mols. (3,800 ml.) of cold anhydrous pyridine. The addition should be done dropwise, and efficient stirring is required, with cooling, to keep the mixture below 10°C. Hydrochloric acid fumes are evolved. 454 gm. of vital wheat gluten are added in small portions to produce a smooth uniform suspension. This is a difficult operation, and a laboratory blender may be required. The suspension is now heated to 75°C for 2 hours, slow stirring being continued throughout. The next operation is to cool and pour the reaction mixture into 16,000 ml. of a 50/50 mixture of N sodium hydroxide and methyl alcohol. After settling has taken place, the supernatant liquor is removed by siphoning and the residue is washed by stirring with an alcoholic solution of sodium hydroxide (4,000 ml. of 0·25N sodium hydroxide and 12,000 ml. of methyl alcohol) and decanting. This is repeated with 16,000 ml. of 75% methyl alcohol in water. The residue is then suspended in 6,000 ml. of 50% methyl alcohol in water and N sodium hydroxide is added slowly to obtain a pH of 7·5.

The product is purified by repeated washing in aqueous methyl alcohol until only a slight precipitation is obtained with barium chloride. Finally the product is dehydrated with acetone, filtered and dried at room temperature under vacuum. The yield of dried powder is about 200 gm., representing just over 40% of the weight of gluten.

Sulphuric Acid Process

2 litres of concentrated sulphuric acid are cooled to about 0°C in an ice/salt bath, 100 gm. of vital gluten are thoroughly stirred into the acid, and stirring is continued for 1 hour, at which time the cooling-bath is removed and the stirring continued until the acid mixture reaches room temperature. The reaction mixture is then poured on to ice, with care being taken to avoid local over-heating. The mixture is now diluted to about 5 gallons, and the insoluble matter filtered off through an acid-resistant cloth. The filtered gluten is now washed by suspending in 3 litres of water and is then refiltered. If difficulty in filtration is experienced the moist gluten should be treated with acetone, which will give a granular precipitate. The sodium salt is prepared by adjusting a suspension in water to pH 7·5 with dilute sodium hydroxide solution. The thick aqueous suspension of the sodium gluten sulphate is washed with distilled water in a solid-bowl centrifuge until free from inorganic sulphates. The washed gel is dehydrated with acetone, filtered, and dried *in vacuo*. The yield of dry gluten sulphate is of the same order as the previous preparation, namely 40–50%.

Both these preparations absorb between 100–300 times their weight of water very quickly to form an odourless, non-toxic and tasteless gel. The use of this compound in pharmaceutical preparations and in the food industry seems to merit some consideration. The method and expense of the preparation are, however, serious drawbacks.

GLUTEN PHOSPHATE

An adaptation of the method used for the phosphorylation of cellulose (49) can be made to produce a gluten phosphate (50). The properties of the gluten phosphate are very similar to those of gluten sulphate, and the cost of manufacture is substantially reduced. Details of the preparation are as follows:

Phosphoric Acid and Urea Process

300 gm. of wet gluten (or corresponding weight of dry), 30 gm. of urea and 18·2 ml. of 85% orthophosphoric acid are mixed together by some suitable mixer. The soft mixture is spread on to a tray in a ¼-in. layer and dried at about 50°C. After 24 hours the dried material is cut up, and the drying is continued until the pieces are brittle enough to be ground in a hammer mill (about 4 days). The ground material is then heated at 140°C for 30 minutes under vacuum. 100 gm. of the resulting powder are suspended in water and 0·1 N sodium hydroxide added to adjust the pH to 7·6. After diluting to about 7 litres, the mixture is allowed to stand for 20 minutes. After decanting, the residue is washed three times with 7-litre portions of 70% acetone, and once finally with 100% acetone. The gluten phosphate is now dried *in vacuo* or in an air-stream.

Gluten phosphate, so prepared, absorbs about 200 times its weight of water. The yield from the dry weight of gluten is over 40%.

AMINO-ACIDS

When wheat gluten is treated with acid, alkali or some proteases, the peptide linkages of the protein molecule are broken and the protein is converted into the constituent amino-acids. The residual starch in the commercial gluten combines in part to form the black humin which is always associated with this reaction. Residual fat also increases the humin formed.

The gluten used for this reaction need not be vital gluten, but it should be of as high a protein content as possible. The range of amino-acids obtained from gluten is listed below. The values are computed for a theoretical gluten having a protein content of 100% (17·5% N), expressed as grams of amino-acid per 100 gm. protein.

Alanine	2·2	Histidine	2·3	Proline	12·7
Arginine	4·7	Isoleucine	4·6	Serine	4·7
Aspartic acid	3·7	Leucine	7·6	Threonine	2·6
Cystine	1·9	Lysine	1·8	Tryptophane	1·1
Glutamic acid	35·5	Methionine	1·9	Tyrosine	3·1
Glycine	3·5	Phenylalanine	5·4	Valine	4·7

Reference (51).

Ammonia is also produced at the rate of 4·5 gm. per 100 gm. of protein and is converted to ammonium chloride. This probably comes from the amides, glutamine and asparagine, which are converted into glutamic acid and aspartic acid. Small amounts of hydrogen sulphide are also formed in the hydrolysis.

Solubilities of the isomers of some of the above amino-acids in gm. per 100 gm. of water at 25°C

DL or L-Alanine	16·7	DL-Methionine	3·4
DL-Aspartic acid	0·78	L-Phenylalanine	3·0
L-Cystine	0·011	DL-Phenylalanine	1·4
L-Glutamic acid	0·86	L-Proline	162
DL-Glutamic acid	2·1	DL-Serine	5·0
Glycine	25·0	L-Tryptophane	1·1
L-Histidine	4·2	D or L-Tyrosine	0·045
DL-Isoleucine	2·2	DL-Tyrosine	0·035
L-Leucine	2·4	L-Valine	8·9
DL-Leucine	0·99	DL-Valine	7·1

Of these amino-acids the best known and most widely used is glutamic acid. Glutamic acid was first isolated in 1866 from the hydrolysate of wheat gluten by sulphuric acid (52). Ritthausen was the discoverer and he determined the empirical formula. The structure of this amino-acid was established in 1890 by the synthesis from laevulinic acid (53). The form in which glutamic acid is best known is as its salt, monosodium glutamate (M.S.G.), which is used in ever-increasing quantities in the food industry. It is a white crystalline salt which has no taste of its own but which, when added to many foods, intensifies the flavour by sensitising the taste buds of the mouth. M.S.G. is also capable of suppressing certain undesirable flavours. This is the naturally occurring form, L(+)-glutamic acid, being one of three forms in which the acid and its salt can be made. The D-glutamic acid has been reported as being present in some bacteria and certain abnormal tissues. DL-glutamic acid is the racemic form. The L(+) form is the only one of interest to food technologists.

L(+)-glutamic acid is an odourless, white crystalline material, decomposing at 213°C and having a specific rotation of +31·2° at 25°C in 5% hydrochloric acid solution $[\alpha]_D^{25}$. It is only slightly soluble in water but very soluble in alkaline solution because of the formation of salts. Glutamic acid has the usual sour taste, but as the acid is neutralised by saliva the characteristic glutamate effect is observed.

Alanine $\quad CH_3 \cdot CH \cdot (\overset{+}{N}H_3) \cdot \overset{-}{COO}$

Arginine $\quad NH_2 - \overset{\overset{\displaystyle NH}{\|}}{C} - NH \cdot CH_2 \cdot CH_2 \cdot CH_2 \cdot CH \cdot (\overset{+}{N}H_3)\overset{-}{COO}$

Aspartic acid $\quad HO \cdot CO \cdot CH_2 \cdot CH(\overset{+}{N}H_3)\overset{-}{COO}$

Cystine $\quad \overset{-}{O} \cdot CO \cdot CH(\overset{+}{N}H_3)CH_2 \cdot S - S \cdot CH_2 \cdot CH(\overset{+}{N}H_3)\overset{-}{COO}$

Glutamic acid $\quad OH \cdot CO \cdot CH_2 \cdot CH_2 \cdot CH(\overset{+}{N}H_3)\overset{-}{COO}$

Glycine $\quad \overset{+}{N}H_3 - CH_2 - \overset{-}{COO}$

Histidine $\quad \begin{array}{l} CH = N - C - CH_2 - CH(\overset{+}{N}H_3)\overset{-}{COO} \\ \;|\qquad\quad\; \| \\ NH \text{——} CH \end{array}$

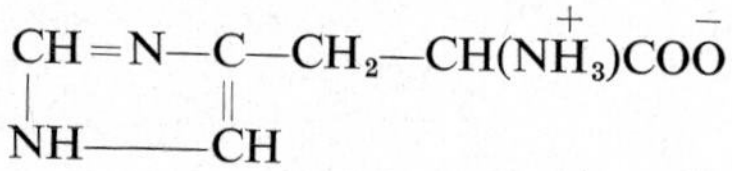

Isoleucine $\quad \begin{array}{l} C_2H_5 - CH \cdot CH(\overset{+}{N}H_3)\overset{-}{COO} \\ \qquad\quad | \\ \qquad\quad CH_3 \end{array}$

Leucine $\quad \begin{array}{l} CH_3 - CH \cdot CH_2 \cdot CH(\overset{+}{N}H_3)\overset{-}{COO} \\ \qquad\quad | \\ \qquad\quad CH_3 \end{array}$

Lysine $\quad H_2N \cdot CH_2 \cdot CH_2 \cdot CH_2 \cdot CH_2 \cdot CH(\overset{+}{N}H_3)\overset{-}{COO}$

Methionine $\quad CH_3 - S - CH_2 \cdot CH_2 \cdot CH(\overset{+}{N}H_3)\overset{-}{COO}$

Phenylalanine $\quad \bigcirc - CH_2 \cdot CH(\overset{+}{N}H_3)\overset{-}{COO}$

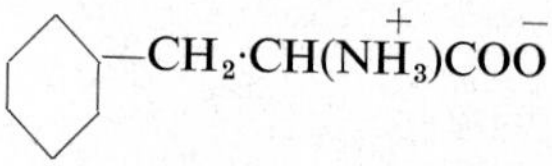

Proline $\quad \begin{array}{l} CH_2 - CH_2 \\ \;|\qquad\quad\;\; \searrow \\ CH_2 - \overset{+}{N}H_2 \nearrow CH \cdot \overset{-}{COO} \end{array}$

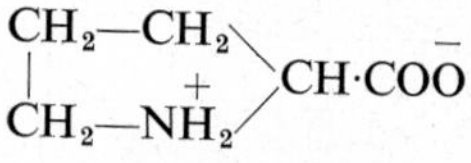

Serine $\quad HO \cdot CH_2 \cdot CH(\overset{+}{N}H_3)\overset{-}{COO}$

Threonine $\quad \begin{array}{l} \qquad OH \\ \qquad | \\ CH_3 \cdot CH \cdot CH(\overset{+}{N}H_3)\overset{-}{COO} \end{array}$

Tryptophane $\quad \begin{array}{l} \bigcirc\!\!\!-C \cdot CH_2 \cdot CH(\overset{+}{N}H_3)\overset{-}{COO} \\ \qquad\;\diagup CH \\ \quad NH \end{array}$

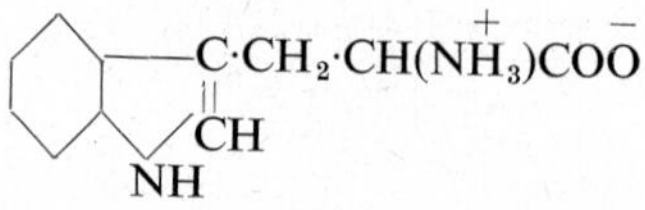

Tyrosine $\quad \begin{array}{l} \bigcirc - CH_2 \cdot CH(\overset{+}{N}H_3)\overset{-}{COO} \\ HO \end{array}$

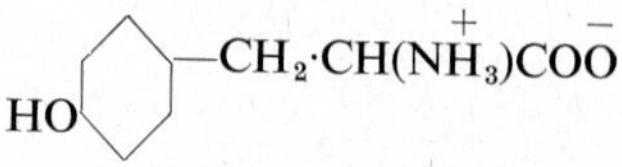

Valine $\quad \begin{array}{l} CH_3 \cdot CH \cdot CH(\overset{+}{N}H_3)\overset{-}{COO} \\ \qquad | \\ \qquad CH_3 \end{array}$

FIG. 41. Structural formulae of some amino-acids.

This is not only a stimulation of the taste buds but also a warm 'rounded' feeling with a strong flow of saliva.

Glutamic acid has been studied in the treatment of mentally retarded children, and continued oral doses up to 24 gm. per day caused increased motor activity or distractability, with no side effects being noted (54).

From wheat gluten the two main products prepared are hydrolysed vegetable protein (H.V.P.), and monosodium glutamate (M.S.G.), and they are obtained by acid hydrolysis. The enzyme method is too slow and incomplete, while hydrolysis under alkaline conditions liberates at least part of the glutamic acid in the racemic or DL-form, and thus gives a poor yield of the L-variety.

In both products it is important to get a high yield of L-glutamic acid, and the optimum conditions have been worked out (55).

100 gm. of wheat gluten (11·3% N) were processed in each case and the hydrolysate made up to 1,000 ml. with distilled water. This solution was then assayed for L-glutamic acid content by a microbiological method (*see* Chapter 4).

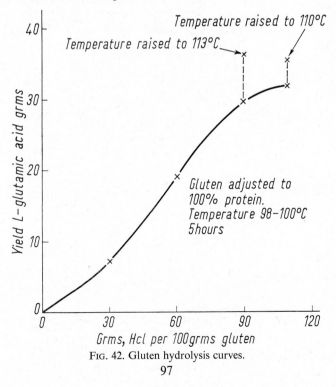

FIG. 42. Gluten hydrolysis curves.

Reagent	Gm. of Reagent 100 ml. Soln.	Vol. of Soln. ml.	Gm. of Reagent per 100 gm. Gluten	Temp. (°C)	Time (Hr.)	Total Yield L-glutamic Acid
NaOH	12	400	48	98–100	0·5	0·49
,,	12	400	48	98–100	1	1·46
,,	12	400	48	98–100	3	2·81
,,	12	400	48	98–100	4	5·40
,,	12	400	48	98–100	5	5·78
,,	12	400	48	110	5	4·99
,,	15	400	60	98–100	5	5·32
,,	30	400	120	98–100	5	11·50
,,	36·2	400	144·8	98–100	5	11·30
,,	50	400	200	98–100	5	12·40
,,	60	400	240	98–100	5	12·20
HCl	10	200	20	98–100	5	4·6
,,	20	200	40	98–100	5	12·3
,,	30	200	60	98–100	5	19·1
,,	36·5	200	73	98–100	5	20·5
,,	30	200	60	113	5	23·4
,,	36·5	200	73	110	5	22·9

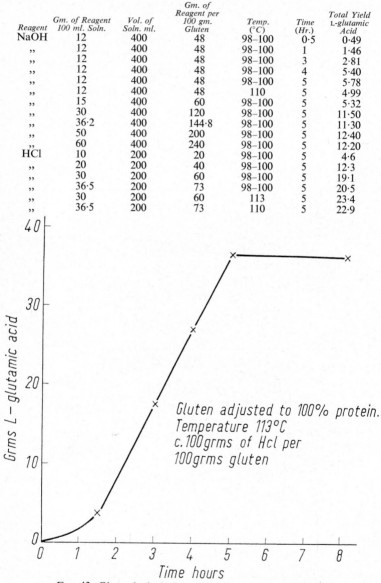

Gluten adjusted to 100% protein.
Temperature 113°C
c. 100 grms of Hcl per
100 grms gluten

FIG. 43. Gluten hydrolysis curve—time/yield relationship.

Fig. 42 shows the yield of L-glutamic acid obtained with differing amounts of hydrochloric acid and at different temperatures. Fig. 43

shows the relationship between time and yield under optimum conditions.

From the results it can be seen that the best yield of L-glutamic acid is obtained by the use of hydrochloric acid. Using caustic soda the yield is lower, because a proportion of the formed glutamic acid is in the racemic form, and is not estimated by the method used. Using hydrochloric acid and five hours for the hydrolysis period, the optimum conditions are a temperature of 113°C and not less than 30% acid solution. This also means approximately one part of hydrochloric acid by weight to each part of protein present.

A useful but not absolutely accurate method is described in a recent publication (56) for the rapid estimation of glutamic acid. Optimum conditions for the hydrolysis of wheat gluten are also discussed.

HYDROLYSED VEGETABLE PROTEIN (H.V.P.)

In commercial production of H.V.P. it is usually the practice to use a lower concentration of hydrochloric acid and to extend the reaction time (Fig. 44). A typical process is now described.

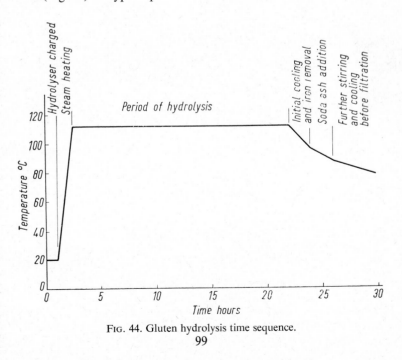

FIG. 44. Gluten hydrolysis time sequence.

The reactor is a steel pressure vessel with some rocking or stirring device. All the surfaces in contact with the acid mixture are lined with resistant rubber or polymer lining. Steam is injected into the vessel after it has been charged, to get a pressure of about 22 p.s.i., and the condensate contributes to the water already in the vessel to give the desired concentration of acid. Rather than use the 30% hydrochloric acid concentration and five hours' cooking, it is convenient to reduce the acid to about 20% and continue the cooking for about 20 hours.

The water and acid are measured into the vessel, and the fine wheat gluten (80% protein content) is added slowly, preferably with stirring. The reactor is fastened down and the steam pressure raised and maintained at about 22 p.s.i. After a period of 20 hours the pressure steam is turned off and the agitation stopped. The temperature is allowed to fall to below the 95°C mark, and some agent is added for the removal of iron which will be present in small quantities. Even in very small quantities the presence of iron produces a bitter-tasting end product. Alkali phosphates are useful in this respect.

After a period of further stirring, soda ash is added very cautiously to neutralise and bring the pH up to 5·3–5·8. Much foaming is evident during the operation.

The next step is the removal of the black humin that has formed. This can be done by means of a filter press, a rotary filter, or by a basket centrifuge. The liquid should be treated while still hot, and the humin cake washed with small quantities of hot water. The filter cloth should be pre-treated with a little diatomaceous earth as an aid to the filtration process. If care is not taken, quite large amounts of the amino-acids can be held back in the humin cake.

It was found, with particular reference to L-glutamic acid, that there is some absorption of this acid on to the humin particles. A typical example of the results obtained is shown (57).

(a) Hydrolysis liquor was taken and filtered warm on a Buchner funnel and the humin cake was given a brief wash with water. The yield of glutamic acid in the filtrate amounted to 8·6 gm.

(b) The same hydrolysis liquor was again filtered warm on a Buchner funnel and the humin cake was transferred to a Soxhlet apparatus and extracted for half an hour with water. This water was added to the filtrate. The yield of glutamic acid in this case was 17·7 gm.

Depending on the protein content of the starting gluten, the weight of dry humin produced will vary between 14% and 18% of the gluten weight.

After the filtration stage the liquor is stored in rubber-lined or wooden vats for a period of maturing. The building in which these vats are contained should be kept at an even temperature. An overnight drop in temperature will cause a crop of sodium chloride crystals, and the liquor will have to be re-heated. A suitable holding temperature is about 20°C, and the period for maturing should be as long as possible, but not less than eight weeks. During this period a further precipitation takes place and the liquor must be polished before finally passing to lined bulk transporters or lined drums. The specific gravity of the liquor at 25°C is about 1·265.

The humin can be further treated with large volumes of hot water, or it can be continuously extracted. The resulting liquors will spray-dry very easily, giving an attractive powder containing as much as

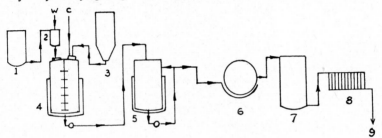

FIG. 44A. Flowsheet for H.V.P. plant.
(1) Bulk acid storage; (2) acid or water measuring tank; (3) bulk gluten storage; (4) jacketed pressure hydrolyser; (5) jacketed holding tank; (6) filter for humin removal; (7) maturing tank; (8) polishing filter; (9) drums or bulk containers for H.V.P.   W = water, C = chemicals.

8·5% w/w of L-glutamic acid. This figure can of course vary, and depends on the previous treatment. The washed humin containing less than 1% of sodium chloride is useful as a soil conditioner, and it has been demonstrated that heavy clay soils are rendered more pliable and easier to work with the use of this material. It is also used, to a small extent, in some types of feeding mixtures for cattle. In this case it is better to use the unextracted humin. Fig. 44A shows a typical layout for an H.V.P. plant.

The matured H.V.P. liquor is a red-brown, clear, sparkling solution. It is an attractive product and a typical analysis is shown below:

Specific gravity at 25°C	1·26
pH at 25°C	5·70
Total solids	48·0% w/w
Total nitrogen	4·50% w/w
Ammonium chloride	4·12% w/w
Sodium chloride	12·47% w/w
L(+)-Glutamic acid	9·17% w/w

The use of H.V.P. for the flavouring of foods has shown interesting and rapid progress throughout the world. The purpose of the inclusion of protein hydrolysates into food is to improve or highlight the flavours, and for many years it has been common practice in China and Japan to use these hydrolysates from various sources, including wheat gluten, as condiments. In a relatively short time the American food industry has become interested and there have been some outstanding improvements in manufacture.

H.V.P. is not a substitute for monosodium glutamate, or vice versa. Each has a distinct role to play in the processing and flavouring of foods. Experiments have indicated that H.V.P., which is a complex mixture of amino-acids, gives a preferred quality rating, a more satisfactory flavour, and generally a more acceptable taste with many foods than when only one of the amino-acids is present.

The four components of taste have been described as sweet, sour, salty and bitter. Now the dextrorotatory forms of glycine, proline, alanine, phenylalanine, serine, leucine and aspartic acid have varying sweet tastes and some flavour. Cystine and methionine have definite tastes and provide pyrogenic flavours when heated. Valine and tyrosine are bitter, and therefore it can be seen that a mixture of all these together with sodium chloride can provide a rounded taste character.

A good, well manufactured H.V.P. liquor obtained from wheat gluten of high protein content will possess an attractive and provoking bouquet. Numerous food products contain H.V.P. in liquor, paste or powder form, and the following list gives some idea of the variety of these products:

Soups	Mincemeat	Poultry
Stews	Sausages	Chow mein
Broths	Goulash	Meat pies
Bouillons	Biscuits	Hash
Fish	Fruit cake	Meat sauces
Gravies	Spices	Cheese spreads
Sandwich spreads	Chop suey	Mayonnaise
Pickle relishes	Chili sauce	Dog foods
Baked beans	Salad dressing	
Pancake flour	Bread	

More recently a new use has been found, that of a bait for fruit-flies. The bait is mixed with a toxic chemical, and the attracted fruit-flies take the bait and are destroyed. The need for protein is believed to account for the fly's attraction and it is a fact that care must be taken during the manufacture of H.V.P. to cover the maturing tanks, otherwise swarms of blowflies (in Australia, the brown *Calliphora* species) die in the liquor, having laid their maggots in the protein-rich material.

102

H.V.P. paste can be produced by evaporating the liquid under vacuum, preferably in all-glass equipment and with the complete absence of metallic surfaces, particularly iron. The resulting paste is coarse because of the salt crystals, and if a smooth paste is desired this can be obtained by treatment through rolls or some other blending device.

The production of a powdered H.V.P. is not quite so straightforward. The finished material should be an attractive light-brown colour, with no evidence of a scorched or bitter taste, and it should not be excessively hygroscopic. The best method for drying the H.V.P. liquid is by spray drying, but this cannot be accomplished unless conditions are correct.

The starch and the fat content of the starting gluten must be as low as possible. In a good quality gluten of 80% protein (dry basis) the normal fat content is about 0·51%, while the figures for gluten dust (ex. the dust collectors in the gluten drying plant) are approximately 80% protein and 1·90% fat. The H.V.P. liquor prepared from the good-quality gluten will spray-dry quite satisfactorily, while the liquor from the dust will not produce a dry, free-flowing powder under the same conditions of heat and feeding rate.

Again it is better to free the starting gluten from the residual carbohydrates by washing with weak acid solution or treatment with an α-amylase. The carbohydrate fraction is converted in the H.V.P. process into dextrines, sugars and humin, and all these substances interfere with the manufacture of a good powder.

The analysis of a good powder is shown below:

	w/w
Moisture	4·0%
pH (10% solution)	5·4
Total nitrogen	8·8%
Ammonium chloride	7·8%
Sodium chloride	24·8%
L(+)-Glutamic acid	18·2%

MONOSODIUM GLUTAMATE

There is a big demand for the single amino-acid, glutamic acid, in the form of its sodium salt. The process is the same as the H.V.P. production up to and including the filtration of the humin. At this point the filtrate liquor is deeply coloured and it can be considerably decolorised by the use of activated carbon. The resulting filtrate is only a pale straw colour, and the subsequent precipitation or crystallisation of the glutamic acid is more rapid because of the smaller proportion of impurities present. However, the use of carbon at this point gives rise to considerable losses by absorption of the amino-acids on to the carbon, and it is not considered worth while to use the material at this stage.

Usually the humin-free liquor, which contains about 48% solids, is concentrated and adjusted to pH 3·2, which is the isoionic point for glutamic acid, and then circulated with cooling for about 3 days. At this time about 75% of the glutamic acid in the liquor will have come down as a fine white precipitate. This can be filtered off and the mother liquor concentrated and sold as H.V.P., or spray-dried to give a powdered H.V.P. The precipitate is not pure glutamic acid, but contains some inorganic materials as impurities.

Another method is to isolate the glutamic acid as its hydrochloride. The acid hydrolysate is concentrated and cooled and the glutamic acid hydrochloride, which is only slightly soluble in hydrochloric acid, crystallises out and about 85% of the glutamic acid in the liquor comes down. The precipitate is filtered off and dissolved in a minimum quantity of water (33/100 parts water) and the pH adjusted to 3·2 with sodium hydroxide, whereupon the glutamic acid crystallises out.

These crude glutamic acid crops must now be washed and this can be done by agitation in warm water and then spinning the crystals. The washed acid is converted to the monosodium salt by reaction with the theoretical quantity of sodium hydroxide and then the near-neutral solution is treated with activated carbon. A crystalline M.S.G. is obtained by slow evaporation of the filtered liquid.

By adjusting the pH of the acid hydrolysate after the humin filtration in the H.V.P. process, crops of other amino-acids can be filtered off before the main recovery of the glutamic acid is undertaken.

The various isoionic points of the amino-acids are shown in the following table:

Glycine	pH 5·97	Methionine	pH 5·74
Alanine	,, 6·00	Tyrosine	,, 5·66
Valine	,, 5·96	Diiodotyrosine	,, 4·29
Leucine	,, 5·98	Cysteine	,, 5·07
Isoleucine	,, 6·02	Aspartic acid	,, 2·77
Serine	,, 5·68	Glutamic acid	,, 3·22
Proline	,, 6·30	Histidine	,, 7·59
Phenylalanine	,, 5·48	Arginine	,, 10·76
Tryptophane	,, 5·89	Lysine	,, 9·74

Reference (58).

With amino-acids the isoelectric point and the isoionic point are just about identical.

Monosodium glutamate is a white crystalline substance resembling sugar or salt in appearance. This chemical has a unique property of improving desirable food flavours. It has no taste of its own but sensitises the taste buds of the mouth. By bringing out and reinforcing the naturally occurring flavours the process can be described as an enhancing, rounding or blending of flavours. It brings out the freshness of newly gathered vegetables, and greatly emphasises the natural flavour of chicken. In some cases there is a suppression of undesirable flavours, such as the sharpness in onions, the earthiness of potatoes and the fishlike flavour sometimes present in lima beans.

Monosodium glutamate is equally effective in maintaining the flavour of processed foods where there is a long interval of time between preparation and consumption. Canned products are improved by its use, and frozen foods hold their flavour longer in storage.

Confectionery, fruit, juices and beverages are not improved by the use of this material.

4

LABORATORY METHODS

In this chapter a number of methods are described for the examination of wheat starch and gluten and their various conversion products. The selected group of methods is not comprehensive but consists rather of those which are in daily use and which are giving useful and repeatable results.

FORMOL METHOD FOR AMINO-ACIDS

Amino-acids cannot be estimated by direct titration with standard solutions because of the opposing effects of the —NH_2 groups and the —COOH groups. However, the reaction between the amino-acids and formaldehyde permits such an estimation to be made.

Taking glycine as an example, the following reaction takes place:

$$HCHO + H_2N \cdot CH_2 \cdot COOH \rightarrow CH_2 = N \cdot CH_2 \cdot COOH$$

The basic NH_2 has disappeared and the carboxyl group can now be titrated directly with a standard sodium hydroxide solution.

Formaldehyde solutions contain traces of formic acid, and the amino-acids are seldom neutral. Therefore, both of the reagents must be brought to the same pH before mixing and it is convenient to make both solutions just alkaline to phenolphthalein with dilute sodium hydroxide solution.

Procedure

Place about 50 ml. of formalin solution (40%) in a flask and add about 12 drops of phenolphthalein solution. Carefully add 0·1 N sodium hydroxide solution until a faint pink colour is evident in the formalin solution. Make up an accurate solution of the amino-acid or acids to contain about 2 gm. in 250 ml. and take 25 ml. of this solution, add 2 drops of phenolphthalein, and add the 0·1 N sodium hydroxide solution until the same depth of pink colour is obtained as before.

To the amino-acid solution add excess of the formalin solution (about 15 ml.). The pink colour disappears immediately and the solution is now acid. Titrate with 0·1 N sodium hydroxide solution until the pink colour is restored.

$$\frac{\text{The titre} \times 10}{10} \equiv \text{ml. of N sodium hydroxide} \equiv \text{Total amino-}$$

acid in 2 gm. of sample.

Taking glycine as an example, then 1 ml. of N sodium hydroxide $\equiv$ 0·075 gm. glycine or 0·014 gm. of amino nitrogen. For a mixture of amino-acids, an approximation can be made and the following relationship used: 1 ml. of N sodium hydroxide $\equiv$ 0·014 gm. amino nitrogen.

GLUTEN

In order to anticipate the performance of a flour in the starch extracting plant, it is often necessary to carry out a laboratory preparation. The behaviour of the dough during washing can be observed and the nature of the extracted gluten examined. Also, approximate yields of starch and gluten can be anticipated. A convenient method is as follows:

Take 100 gm. of the flour in question and, using a spatula, mix to a dough with about 70 ml. of the factory water supply. This figure can vary according to the flour strength. This operation can be carried out in a beaker or a dish which is large enough to allow manual manipulation of the dough. 500 ml. of factory water are now put into the container, and if necessary the dough piece is flattened so that it is completely covered by the water. Leave for 1 hour.

At the end of this period the matured dough is squeezed and massaged gently with one hand covered in a smooth rubber glove. After 5 minutes' treatment, during which time the dough should be retained as much as possible in one piece, the starch slurry is carefully poured into another beaker through a fine silk. Care must be taken to lose no starch and the material retained on the silk should be washed back into the beaker containing the gluten/dough with another 500 ml. of water. The squeezing treatment is repeated for another 5 minutes. The behaviour of the dough and its tendency to break up can be noted during these operations. The washing and decanting operation is continued with further 500-ml. fractions of factory water, making a total water volume used of 2,000 ml.

The wet mass of gluten is now weighed and examined for extensibility. A moisture and protein content estimation can be carried out. The starch slurry is allowed to settle and the clear or comparatively clear supernatant liquor siphoned off to within an inch of the starch surface. The starch is now thoroughly stirred and the volume noted by decanting to a stoppered measuring cylinder. An aliquot portion of the thoroughly mixed starch slurry is taken and spun in a tube centrifuge. The compressed starch in the tube will be topped by a gluten layer and this must be carefully scraped off with a small spatula after the residual liquid has been decanted. The starch can now be washed out of the tube, filtered and dried. A protein content determination should be carried out, and from the weight of dry starch the commercial yield can be calculated.

MOISTURE

A useful method for this determination, particularly in product-control laboratories where many of these moisture figures have to be determined as quickly as possible, is that done in the Carter-Simon oven. The time for the determination is 15 minutes and the results are about 0·5% higher than those obtained in the much longer determination described later in this section.

The Carter-Simon oven operates at 155°C, and the samples are contained in aluminium dishes, the sample weight being 5 gm. The oven has hinged doors that permit the dishes to be inserted and moved through the oven in one direction only. A tared pan and lid should be prepared and 5 gm. of sample weighed into the pan. Place the lid on top of the oven and introduce the pan and contents into the oven. Similarly, introduce pans at 5, 10 and 15 minute intervals. At this time the first pan will have been pushed out of the oven and the lid must be placed on firmly and the dish allowed to cool for 5 minutes. It can then be re-weighed and the loss in weight × 20 is equal to the per cent moisture content.

A longer method and one which is more accurate is as follows:

Weigh out accurately about 5 gm. of the sample into a tared glass dish provided with a well-fitting lid. Place the uncovered dish and its lid into an oven set at 100°C and hold it there for 4 hours. At the expiry of this time remove the dish, with lid in place, to cool in a desiccator and re-weigh. Return the uncovered dish and lid into the oven and leave for a further half hour. Again determine the loss and confirm that little or no further loss has taken place.

DOUGH TESTING—BRABENDER FARINOGRAPH

To examine the behaviour of a flour in the form of its dough, or to evaluate the quality of a sample of gluten, no better machine can be suggested than the Brabender Farinograph. This piece of equipment is well-tried and used extensively. The principle of the Farinograph is the measurement of the force required to drive mixer blades at a constant speed through the test dough. A recording pen draws a wide band which is altered in shape according to the changes in the dough and which is known as a Farinogram.

The Farinograph consists of a mixer driven by a motor. The mixer is two-bladed, the speeds of the blades being 56 r.p.m. and 84 r.p.m. The usual quantity of flour used for a test is 300 gm., and the mixer is water-jacketed to maintain it at a known temperature, usually 30°C. There is a separate unit, consisting of a water tank, electric heating element and thermostat, to provide the circulating water for the mixer jacket.

The torque reaction of the motor driving the mixing blades, controlled by the stiffness of the dough, is transmitted through an

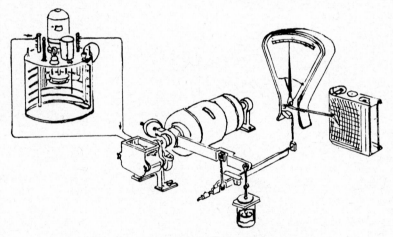

FIG. 45. Brabender Farinograph.

arrangement of levers to a recording pen. During the test the pen traces a band which varies in its position on the scale according to the consistency of the dough. The peak is shown when the dough is at maximum resistance and the curve falls away as the gluten breaks down under the mechanical action of the mixers. The machine is shown in Fig. 45.

Before a flour test can be carried out on the Farinograph, the water absorption of the flour must be determined. The test is carried out at a fixed flour consistency which can be the 500 or 600 line on the recording graph paper. 300 gm. of the flour are weighed into the mixer and the blades are set in motion. Water at 30°C is added from a burette until a dough has been formed which records a level curve for a few moments on the desired 500 or 600 level. The burette reading then gives the flour/water absorption which is used in the test proper.

Another 300 gm. of flour are weighed out and the mixer is again started. The whole amount of water at 30°C is run in and any portions of flour clinging to the sides are scraped down to give a single clean mass of dough. The mixer should be covered with a small sheet of glass. A curve will be traced, rising to its peak and thereafter falling away. The 500 or 600 line will pass through the middle of the curve at its peak section.

When a sample of gluten is being tested, this is mixed with a flour which has known characteristics and the curve traced for the mixture. The influence of the added gluten can then be deducted from the altered shape of the curve. 300 gm. of admixture are used with the quantity of gluten required to give the desired protein figure in the resulting flour.

An examination of the Farinogram will give information on the flour under test, although the Farinograph does not directly measure any fundamental physical property, and does not exactly imitate any commercial mixing process. The Farinogram should be evaluated by a close look at the whole of the curve rather than at any one part of it and it could be said, perhaps, that the balance of the flour is drawn by the pen. Typical Farinograms for a strong flour and for a weak flour are shown in Fig. 46.

Taking a general curve as shown (Fig. 47) the following interpretations are usual:

C = dough consistency
D = dough development time
S = period of dough stability
B = degree of breakdown in dough stability

DOUGH TESTING—BRABENDER EXTENSOGRAPH

This apparatus measures the resistive forces to extension set up in a fixed dough piece when it is deformed by a moving hook-shaped arm (Fig. 48). The determination is carried out as follows:

The Brabender Farinograph should be used to prepare the dough. Weigh 300 gm. of the flour and place in the mixing-bowl maintained at 30°C. Mix for 5 minutes to bring the flour to bowl temperature. (A previous Farinogram has been done to establish the required amount of distilled water at 30°C which must be added to the flour to give a consistency of 500 Farinograph units.) Add the water required, in which is dissolved 6 gm. of sodium chloride. After

1 minute of mixing switch the mixers off and allow the dough to rest for exactly 5 minutes with a cover over the bowl. At the end of 5 minutes switch the motor on again and mix for a further 2 minutes.

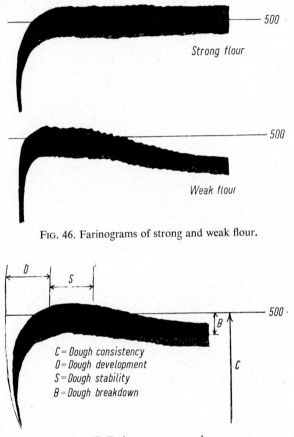

FIG. 46. Farinograms of strong and weak flour.

FIG. 47. Farinogram—general curve.

At the termination of the total mixing time of 3 minutes, the consistency of the dough must be 500 units $\pm$ 10 units. If the consistency is outside these limits the test must be repeated making the necessary alteration in added water.

The dough is now removed from the mixer, taking care not to deform or stretch it. Scale off two 150-gm. pieces of dough, using a pair of scissors to cut the dough. After roughly shaping each piece into a ball on the special moulder by giving 20 turns, they must be immediately placed centrally in the back of the dough roller, rolled and placed in position in the dough holder with as little handling as possible. Press the clamps into position and place the holder into the fermentation cabinet of the Extensograph.

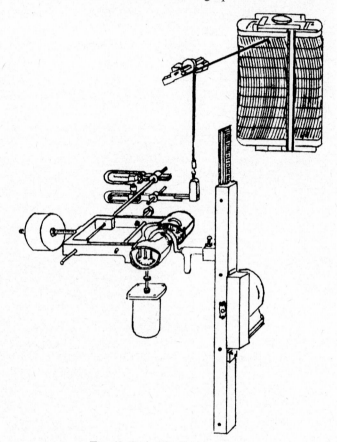

Fig. 48. Brabender Extensograph.

On completion of a 45-minute rest period the dough holder can be placed in position on the cradle of the extension system of the Extensograph and the motor started, whereupon the hook travels downward at 14–15 mm. per second. This is continued until the dough breaks. A pen records the stresses on graph paper.

Make a duplicate test on the second dough piece. The curves obtained should resemble one another if the conditions are right. The dough pieces are re-shaped and re-moulded as before, and second and third tests are carried out after a further 45-minute rest and a final 45-minute rest in the fermentation cabinet.

Typical curves are shown below (Fig. 49):

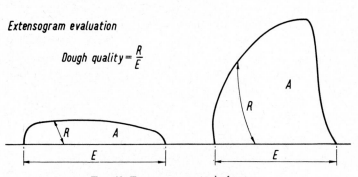

FIG. 49. Extensograms, typical curves.

The following deductions are made from the curves:

(1) The total area enclosed by the curve gives a measure of the strength of the dough, A.
(2) The maximum height of the curve in mm. after 50 mm. stretching gives a measure of the resistance of the dough to extension, R.
(3) The base length measurement in mm. gives the extensibility, E.
(4) The ratio R : E gives an indication of the dough quality. The larger the value for R : E then the shorter will be the dough.

FLOUR SOLUBLES

This determination will be required in the examination of a flour for the protein/starch extraction process. A flour with a high cold-water solubles figure is often not physically suitable for the process and, of course, this is a fraction that will be lost into the effluent during the extraction operation.

Procedure. Weigh out 25 gm. of the flour into a beaker and add about 200 ml. of distilled water. Stir slowly (60 r.p.m.) with a mechanical stirrer for 30 minutes. Allow the beaker contents to settle and decant the supernatant liquid through a No. 5 Whatman filter-paper, making sure that the filtrate is clear. Make up to 250 ml. with water and evaporate an aliquot portion of 50 ml. to dryness in a previously tared silica dish. A water bath is required for this. The dish and the dried residue are now placed in an oven at 100°C and dried to constant weight.

$$\text{The flour solubles } \% = \frac{\text{weight of residue} \times 5}{25} \times 100$$

$$= \text{weight of residue} \times 20$$

PRE-COOKED STARCHES

The following method (59) for determination of viscosity potential has been designed for rapid product control and for intercomparison of pre-cooked starches of similar types. The viscosity ratings obtained by this method do not necessarily apply to consistencies obtained under other conditions:

Materials.

Pre-cooked starch at normal moisture content.
Cereal starches, 30 gm.
Potato, sago, cassava, derivatised cereal, waxy starches, 20 gm.
Acetone, 35 ml. commercial grade.
Sucrose solution, 450 ml. of 50% cane-sugar/water solution.

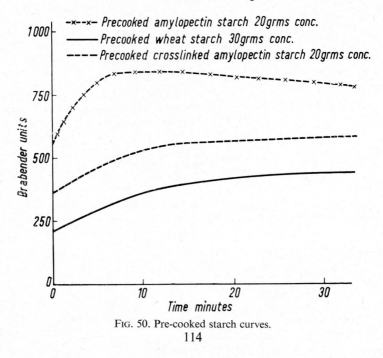

FIG. 50. Pre-cooked starch curves.

The sucrose is checked at exactly 50% on a 95% scale sugar refractometer at 20°C. The sucrose solution alone gives 25 Brabender Units at 30°C ± 0·4°C when checked with an accurate hand thermometer under the conditions of the method.

Method. The pre-cooked starch is placed in a 600-ml. beaker and the acetone is added and stirred with a glass rod. Sucrose solution is poured in with slow hand-stirring. The resulting suspension is poured into a Brabender Viscograph bowl and run in the machine for 30 minutes at 30°C.

The reading in Brabender graph units at 30 minutes is taken as a measure of the viscosity potential of the pre-cooked sample. Examples are shown in Fig. 50.

REDUCING SUGARS

This method for the determination of reducing sugars is by the constant-volume modification of the Lane and Eynon method. It is used in the Laboratory of the Government Chemist, London, and is substantially the same as the method approved by the International Commission for Uniform Methods of Sugar Analysis.

The principle involved in the determination is the titration of Fehling's solution at boiling point with the test-sugar solution, using methylene blue as the indicator. The volumes of the solutions are adjusted so that the total volume at the end of the titration has a specified value.

Reagents. Fehling's solution is prepared by mixing equal volumes of copper sulphate solution, containing 69·28 gm. of A.R. copper sulphate pentahydrate per litre, and a solution containing 346 gm. of A.R. potassium sodium tartrate tetrahydrate and 100 gm. of A.R. sodium hydroxide per litre.

The Fehling's solution is unstable in the presence of air and should be prepared as wanted.

Standard invert sugar solution containing 2·50 gm. of invert sugar per litre, prepared as follows:

Dissolve 0·475 gm. of pure cane sugar in 20 ml. of water and add 20 ml. of hydrochloric acid solution (50 ml. of concentrated hydrochloric acid to 1,000 ml. with water). Bring the mixture to the boil and continue boiling for half a minute, cool rapidly and neutralise the mixture with N sodium hydroxide solution, using litmus paper as an indicator. Now make the solution just acid with hydrochloric acid, because invert sugar is not stable in alkaline solution. Dilute the solution to 200 ml. in a volumetric flask.

Methylene blue indicator. One per cent solution in water.

Proceaure. The first operation is the standardisation of the Fehling's solution. Theoretically, 20 ml. of the Fehling's solution should be reduced by 40 ml. of the standard invert sugar solution under the conditions of the test. If this is not so then it is desirable, for routine work, to adjust the concentration of the copper sulphate solution until the titre is exactly 40 ml. This will mean that if a 0·5% w/v solution of the unknown sample is titrated against 20 ml. of the Fehling's solution, the percentage of reducing sugars in the sample is then 2,000 × the reciprocal of the number of mls. of solution used in the titration. This figure of 2,000 is described as the 'factor' of the Fehling's solution. Alternatively, for non-routine conditions, the actual factor can be used. Using the 'factor' gives results in terms of invert sugar and a factor of 0·97 is required to obtain the dextrose equivalent.

Prepare a solution containing 5·00 gm. of the sample per litre. Pipette 20 ml. of the Fehling's solution into a 500-ml. conical flask. Add a little pumice powder and sufficient distilled water to bring the total volume of Fehling's solution, water and test solution to 75 ml. at the end of the titration. (To determine the amount of water to be added, it is usually necessary to make a preliminary titration using an estimated amount of water.) Add from a burette all but approximately 1 ml. of the required quantity of test solution, place the flask on a silica plate or asbestos-centred gauze and bring to the boil. After two minutes' boiling add two drops of methylene blue indicator and complete the titration by small additions of test solution, allowing 10–15 seconds between each addition until the blue colour is just discharged. The titration should be completed within $1\frac{1}{2}$ to 2 minutes from the addition of the indicator. Boiling should be steady and continuous throughout to exclude the influence of oxygen. For this reason also, the flask should not be shaken once heating has been started.

Results.

$$\text{Reducing sugars as invert sugar} = \frac{\text{'Factor'}}{\text{titre in ml.}}\%$$

$$\text{Dextrose equivalent} = \frac{0·97 \times \text{'Factor'}}{\text{titre in ml.}}\%$$

NITROGEN AND PROTEIN

The estimation of nitrogen in flour, gluten or starch can be done quite accurately by the well-accepted Kjeldahl method. It is normally recognised that N × 5·7 represents the protein in flour and all wheat products, including wheat starch. The factor of 6·25 is used for feeding stuffs, while 6·38 is used for milk compounds and 6·0 for soya products. The details of determination are as follows:

Reagents

Caustic-hypo solution. Approximately 38 gm. of caustic soda flake and 5 gm. of sodium thiosulphate in 100 ml. of solution.

Sulphuric acid A.R. conc., S.G. 1·84.

Mercuric oxide A.R.

Sodium sulphate A.R. anhydrous.

Methyl red indicator, 0·5 gm. in 100 ml. solution.

Procedure. Place 1·000 gm. of a well-mixed representative sample in a 500-ml. long-necked Kjeldahl flask. Add 0·7 gm. of mercuric oxide, 10 to 15 gm. anhydrous sodium sulphate and 25 ml. A.R. concentrated sulphuric acid. Place on a gas or electric heater and digest briskly for 45 minutes. During this time the solution should clear. The sulphuric fumes should be removed by a forced draught.

Remove the flask, cool and add about 200 ml. of distilled water, and cool to 25°C or less. Place the flask in position in a distillation stand without attaching the still-head. Pour 80 ml. of caustic-hypo solution down the inclined neck of the flask and, without mixing, attach the still-head without delay. The condenser still-tube should be dipping below the surface of 25 ml. of 0·5 N hydrochloric acid, containing a few drops of methyl red indicator and contained in a 300-ml. conical flask. The contents of the Kjeldahl flask should be mixed by swirling gently and the distillation started. A steady rate of condensate should be maintained until between 150 ml. and 200 ml. have been collected. Titrate the excess acid with 0·5 N sodium hydroxide using a good-quality burette. The titration figure should then be corrected for the reagent blank.

1 ml. 0·5 N hydrochloric acid ≡ 7·0 mg. nitrogen

≡ 39·9 mg. wheat protein

When wheat starch is being examined for protein content, conditions are altered because of the small amounts of protein present. A sample of 2·5 gm. is taken and the contents of the Kjeldahl flask distilled into 10 ml. of 0·05 N hydrochloric acid. The excess acid is then titrated with 0·05 N sodium hydroxide.

It should be mentioned here that in place of the standard hydrochloric acid in the collecting flask, a 1% boric acid solution can be used to collect the ammonia which is distilled. The ammonia is then titrated directly with the standard solution of hydrochloric acid, using a mixed indicator (e.g. screened methyl red). By this means the

117

preparation and use of a standard sodium hydroxide solution is avoided, although all analytical laboratories will have this available in any case.

PENTOSAN CONTENT IN STARCH AND FLOUR

The pentosan content in wheat flour is quite important when the flour is going to be used for the manufacture of starch and gluten. This pentosan fraction interferes with the clean extraction of the starch, giving low yields, and therefore it is necessary that the flour contains as little pentosan as possible.

Again, when wheat starch is going to be further processed, for example, into glucose, the pentosan fraction of the starch is troublesome, causing difficulty in filtration. In the purification process the extracted starch should be washed well enough to free it substantially from the pentosans. The following method for the determination of total pentosans has been used with success (60).

Reagents. Hydrochloric acid 12% w/w. Add 720 ml. of concentrated hydrochloric acid to 1,170 ml. of distilled water.

Stock iron solution. Dissolve 0·990 gm. of ferric ammonium sulphate in concentrated hydrochloric acid and make up to 1 litre in the same acid.

Orcinol reagent. 333 ml. of stock iron solution.

467 ml. of concentrated hydrochloric acid.

200 ml. of distilled water.

2·0 gm. of orcinol (recrystallised from hot water with a little charcoal and dried in a vacuum desiccator).

Dissolve the orcinol in a portion of the water and add to the mixed acid-water reagents. Store in a refrigerator.

Standard xylose solution. Dissolve 0·500 gm. of D-xylose and 1·0 gm. of sodium benzoate in distilled water and make up to 500 ml. in a volumetric flask with water.

Procedure. Assemble a simple quickfit distillation apparatus (with no fractionation column). Accurately weigh about 0·4 gm. of finely ground sample into a dry 500-ml. round-bottomed flask. Add 100 ml. of 12% hydrochloric acid and a few glass beads. Bring the mixture to the boil, control the heating so that the rate of distillation is 30 ml. every 10 minutes, and run in fresh 12% hydrochloric acid from a dropping funnel after each 10-minute interval to make up the original volume. Distil 360 ml. to 400 ml. in this manner. All the furfural will then have been distilled over. Rinse the condenser down with 12%

hydrochloric acid and transfer the distillate, with washings, to a 500-ml. graduated flask. Make up to the mark with 12% hydrochloric acid and mix well.

Carry out another distillation experiment with the same conditions but using 10 ml. of the standard xylose solution in place of the unknown sample.

To determine the amounts of furfural, pipette accurately 1-ml. and 2-ml. portions of the unknown sample distillate into two 6 in. × 1 in. test-tubes. Add 2 ml. to the first tube and 1 ml. of 12% hydrochloric acid to the second tube to bring the total of each aliquot to 3 ml. Add 9 ml. of the orcinol reagent to each tube and mix well. Cover each tube with a 30-ml. beaker, place in a boiling water bath for 30 minutes, cool rapidly under cold running water and read the optical density of the colour formed in the Spekker spectrophotometer. Use No. 8 filters and 1-cm. cells with water in the reference cell. The reading is used to ascertain the equivalent amount of xylose in the sample by referring to a graph which is drawn from a standard series by pipetting 0, 1·0 ml., 1·5 ml., 2 ml. and 2·5 ml. of the standard xylose distillate into five 6 in. × 1 in. test-tubes and adjusting the volume in each test-tube to 3 ml. with 12% hydrochloric acid. Add 9 ml. of orcinol reagent to each tube and mix well. After covering with 30 ml.-beakers, the tubes should be heated for 30 minutes in a boiling water bath, cooled rapidly and the optical densities determined. A graph can then be constructed of optical density against xylose in milligrams, and the milligrams M of xylose in 1 ml. of the unknown sample distillate can now be read off.

% Pentosan in sample

$$= \frac{M \times 500 \times 0\cdot97}{\text{Sample weight in gm.} \times 10^3} = \frac{0\cdot485M}{\text{gm. sample weight}}$$

STARCH IN PAPER

When a starch is being considered for use in paper manufacture, particularly as a beater additive, the degree of retention in the final paper is an important factor to be known. The following method has given consistent results in the examination of many hand-made test sheets (61).

Reagents. Acetate buffer pH 4·2. Dissolve 41 gm. of sodium acetate anhydrous (68 gm. of hydrated) in 375 ml. of distilled water. Adjust the pH to 4·2 with glacial acetic acid and transfer quantitatively to a 500-ml. graduated flask. Make up to the mark with distilled water.

Amyloglucosidase enzyme solution 0·5%. Prepare each day as required a fresh solution of the enzyme in distilled water at a 0·5% concentration.

Sulphuric acid solution 76%. Carefully add 760 ml. concentrated A.R. sulphuric acid to 200 ml. of distilled water, cool to room temperature and dilute to 1 litre with distilled water.

Anthrone reagent. Prepare fresh solution as required each day. The concentration is 0·1 gm. B.D.H. anthrone in 100 ml. of 76% aqueous sulphuric acid solution.

Standard starch solution. Accurately weigh about 0·2 gm. (*W*) of pure starch of known moisture content *M*% into a weighing dish. Mix to a paste with water and transfer quantitatively to a 400-ml. beaker containing 200 ml. of distilled water. Bring to the boil with constant stirring, and boil for a few minutes. Cool, and dilute to 250 ml. at 20°C.

$$5 \text{ ml.} \equiv \frac{W}{50} \text{ gm. starch (wet basis)}$$

$$\equiv \frac{W}{50} \times \frac{(100 - M)}{100} \text{ gm. starch (dry basis)}$$

Standard graph. Accurately pipette or measure by burette 5-ml., 10-ml. and 15-ml. aliquots of the standard starch solution into 100-ml. graduated flasks. Add to each, 60 ml. of distilled water, 1 ml. of acetate buffer solution and 10 ml. of the enzyme solution. Dilute with water to the mark at 20°C. Mix, stopper and stand in a water bath at 50°C for 2 hours. Cool quickly, mix well and centrifuge for 10 minutes at 2,500 r.p.m.

Carry out an enzyme blank (without starch addition) at the same time as the starch solution and using the same procedure.

Measure by burette 10 ml. of the anthrone reagent into a number of 6 in. × 1 in. test-tubes. Each solution and the enzyme blank should be tested in triplicate whilst a reagent blank should also be done.

Reagent blank. Accurately add 1 ml. of distilled water in drops to the 10 ml. of anthrone reagent with constant agitation. Mix well.

Starch solutions and enzyme blank. Accurately add 1 ml. of the centrifuged solution in drops to the 10 ml. of anthrone reagent with constant agitation. Mix well.

Cover each tube with a 30-ml. beaker and heat in a boiling water bath for exactly 12 minutes. Cool rapidly in running water and measure the optical density of the colour formed on the Spekker spectrophotometer with the reagent blank in the reference cell, using No. 7 filters and 1-cm. cells. The colour is stable for 3 hours.

Subtract the optical density of the enzyme blank from the optical density of the starch solution. Construct a graph from the resulting optical densities of the starch solutions and the known weight of dry starch.

Procedure. Weigh accurately into a 100-ml. screw-cap bottle about 0·5 gm. of the paper sample, torn into small pieces, taken from different parts of the whole finished paper to give a representative sample.

Add 45 ml. of distilled water and macerate for 7 minutes with an electrical stirrer. Detach the bottle, stand a 250-ml. beaker under the stirrer and wash free from fibre, and wash the contents of the bottle into the beaker, keeping the total volume below 70 ml. Boil for 3 minutes, cool and carefully transfer back to the bottle with washing. Total volume not more than 80 ml. Add 1 ml. of acetate buffer solution, 10 ml. of 0·5% enzyme solution. Mix well, fix cap and stand in a water bath at 50°C for 2 hours. After that time cool quickly in ice water, transfer to a 100-ml. flask, make up to the mark with water and mix well. Centrifuge the fibre suspension for 10 minutes at 2,500 r.p.m.

Carry out a blank on 0·5 gm. of paper (without the added starch) at the same time and using the same procedure.

Measure from a burette 10 ml. of freshly prepared anthrone reagent into a number of dry 6 in. × 1 in. test-tubes. Each sample should be done in triplicate, the paper blank in triplicate and a reagent blank.

Reagent blank. Add 1 ml. of distilled water drop by drop to the 10 ml. of anthrone reagent, with constant agitation. Mix well.

Test samples and paper blank. Add 1 ml. of the centrifuged solution in drops to the 10 ml. of anthrone reagent with constant agitation. Mix well.

Cover each tube with a 30-ml. beaker and heat in a boiling water bath for exactly 12 mins. Cool rapidly in running water. Measure the optical density on the Spekker spectrophotometer with the reagent blank in the reference cell, using No. 7 filters and 1-cm. cells.

Subtract the optical density of the paper blank from that of the test solution and read off from the standard graph the weight of dry starch.

From this figure the amount of dry starch in the original paper is easily worked out. This method can be used for the estimation of starch in cereal products. However, extraction of the natural sugars in the test material must first be carried out. Weigh 0·2 gm. of the finely ground sample into a 50-ml. centrifuge tube, add 2 drops of 80% ethyl alcohol for mixing and then 5 ml. of water, and stir thoroughly. Add 25 ml. of hot 80% alcohol and stir well. Set aside for 5 minutes and then centrifuge. Decant the alcoholic solution and repeat the extraction. The alcohol should be removed from the extract by evaporation and the extract diluted so that 1 ml. of the solution contains about 50 microgrammes of dextrose. 1 ml. is used for the estimation with the anthrone as already described. This figure for the natural sugars in the sample must be deducted from the total starch and sugar estimated as total starch in the subsequent test on the sample.

STARCH BULK VOLUME

For this test a bumping box is required. This is shown in Fig. 51. It consists of a 100-ml. measuring cylinder held in a framework by

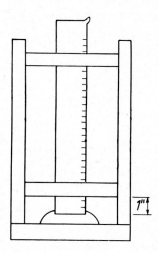

two wooden collars which allow the cylinder to be raised and dropped a distance of 1 in. It is advisable to have several cylinders of the correct dimensions in reserve.

Procedure. Weigh 20 gm. of the starch into the cylinder and place this in position in the bumping box. Using a stop-watch for timing, lift the cylinder and allow it to drop once every 2 seconds for 60 drops. Note the volume (x). Give a further 20 drops and note the volume again (y). If x/y is not 1·0 the test should be repeated. The final figure (y) is used and the volume per unit weight is recorded.

This test is particularly useful when, for example, a pre-cooked starch is being manufactured for final packaging into a small container, and the product has to be manufactured to a tight specification. Any serious divergence in bulk volume can mean that the required weight cannot be put into a packet or that the packet looks only half full when opened by the housewife.

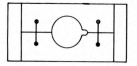

FIG. 51. Bumping box.

AMINO-ACIDS

The following method has been adopted from recently published work (62) and is an approximate but quick determination of aspartic-glutamic acids and the total amino-acids in protein hydrolysates. Basically the scheme is to absorb all the amino-acids on to an acid exchange-resin and to separate the sugars and nitrogen-free acids by washing with water. Elution with ammonium hydroxide gives an ammoniacal solution of the amino-acid-ammonium salts. The free ammonia is driven off by boiling and the cool solution is then applied to a weakly acid exchange-resin, which converts the ammonium salts into the free amino-acids. The amino-acids can now be titrated with standard sodium hydroxide solution to a pH of 6·5 determined

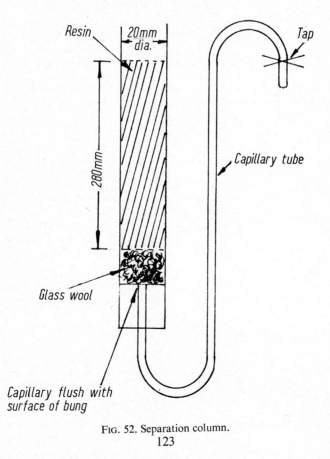

Fig. 52. Separation column.

123

electrometrically, at which point one carboxylic group of the dibasic amino-acids (glutamic and aspartic) has been saturated.

To determine the total amino-acids, a formol titration is subsequently carried out.

Apparatus. 1 column containing strongly acid exchange-resin Amberlite IR 120 (Technical).

1 column containing weakly acid exchange-resin Amberlite IRC 50 (Technical).

Each column consists of a glass tube approximately 20 mm. in diameter and in excess of 280 mm. in length. The resin is supported in the column by a coarse glass sinter or by a plug of glass wool. A capillary tube is fitted to the bottom of the tube and arranged as shown in Fig. 52.

The resin is loaded into the column by slurrying the resin in N hydrochloric acid and pouring into the column. Air must be carefully excluded from the column; if any air bubbles are observed, the column should be emptied and the filling procedure repeated. Once the columns are filled the liquor level must not fall below the surface of the resin. The resin will swell after being wet for 24 hours, and the height of the resin is then adjusted.

Conditioning the resins. Both Amberlite IR 120 and IRC 50 are treated in the same way. N hydrochloric acid is allowed to flow through the column from a dropping-funnel at the rate of 1–2 drops per second, keeping the head of the liquid in the column constant at about $\frac{1}{4}$ in. above the surface of the resin, until the eluate is definitely acid. The column is then washed through with distilled water in the same manner until the eluate is free from chloride (silver nitrate test). About 400 ml. to 500 ml. water are required.

Saturating the columns with amino-acids. Both resins will absorb amino-acids into the resin and therefore it is essential to saturate them before proceeding with determinations. This saturation procedure is carried out in an identical manner to the 'determination' described later. It has been observed that the saturation procedure must be carried out four times before consistent results are obtained. Once this saturation is complete the resins can be used constantly.

Determination. The test solution should be dilute and not contain more than approx. 0·1 gm. of glutamic acid in 100 ml. 100 ml. of test solution are fed into column IR 120 from a dropping-funnel at 1–2 drops per second. Follow this with distilled water in the same way until the eluate is free from chloride. Discard all the wash water. Now apply 350 ml. 2 N ammonium hydroxide to elute all the amino-acids and collect the whole of this eluate. Boil for 20 minutes to expel the excess ammonia and then cool. Pass the cooled liquor through the second column IRC 50 followed by 200 ml. distilled water, and make the total volume to 500 ml. Titrate electrometrically the 500 ml. with 0·05 N sodium hydroxide to pH 6·5. This will take x ml. 0·05 N sodium hydroxide. Now add 20 ml. of 35% formalin which has previously been adjusted to pH 6·5 and continue the titration to pH 9·0. This will take the final titration of y ml. 0·05 N sodium hydroxide (y ml. includes x ml.).

Now x ml. represents the glutamic and aspartic acids, and since in wheat gluten the ratio of these acids is 10 : 1, the factor which is required for glutamic acid alone is 0·91. Therefore 0·91x ml. of 0·05 N sodium hydroxide represents the glutamic acid.

1 ml. of 0·05 N sodium hydroxide corresponds to 0·00735 gm. of glutamic acid. y ml. represents the total amino-acids.

Reconditioning the resins. Wash column IR 120 until it is free from ammonium hydroxide and then apply N hydrochloric acid until the eluate is acid.

Wash column IRC 50 with N hydrochloric acid until the eluate is acid. Then wash both columns with water until no chloride is detected in the eluate. The columns are then ready for further estimations.

AN EXACT MICROBIOLOGICAL METHOD FOR L-GLUTAMIC ACID

The method is based on the use of an enzyme which specifically decarboxylates L-glutamic acid. This glutamic decarboxylase which is widely distributed in micro-organisms liberates one mole of carbon dioxide from the glutamic acid to yield γ-amino butyric acid. The procedure is essentially to prepare a pure sample of the decarboxylase and to react with a known weight of glutamic acid sample. The volume of carbon dioxide evolved is measured, and by knowing that 1 mole of carbon dioxide equals 1 mole of L-glutamic acid, the percentage of the acid in the sample can be calculated. The Warburg apparatus is used for the assay.

The Warburg apparatus. The essential principle employed is that at constant temperature and constant gas volume, changes in the amount of a gas can be measured by changes in the pressure. The apparatus consists of a detachable flask equipped with a side-arm and attached to a manometer containing liquid of known density (Fig. 53). The flask is immersed in a water bath at a constant temperature and between readings the system is shaken to provide a rapid gas exchange between the fluid and the gas phase (Fig. 54). It is assumed that the temperature of the manometer, which is not immersed, does not

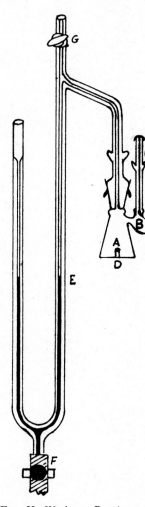

FIG. 54. Water bath and agitator for the Warburg Respirometer.

FIG. 53. Warburg Respirometer. (A) flask; (B) side-arm; (C) side-arm stopper with gas vent; (D) centre well; (E) manometer proper; (F) fluid reservoir—adjustment of the screw clamp alters the level of the fluid in the manometer; (G) three-way stopcock.

126

differ greatly from that of the flask. The manometer has an open end and a closed end. A given point on the closed side of the manometer (150 mm.) is chosen, and the liquid in the closed arm of the manometer is always adjusted to this point before recording pressure changes.

To carry out a determination, the volume of the flask and manometer down to the 150-mm. mark must be known. The following method for finding this (63) is simple and easy to follow:

An extra small conical flask B of about 10 ml. capacity, which is fitted with a ground stopper A, is required. The stopper should be of

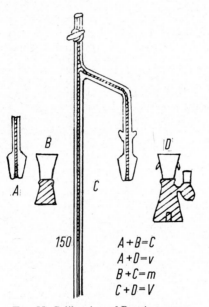

$$A + B = C$$
$$A + D = v$$
$$B + C = m$$
$$C + D = V$$

Fig. 55. Calibration of Respirometer.

the standard taper and size for the apparatus and should have a short capillary tube attached so that with flask B it is an effective specific-gravity bottle. Mercury is used for the calibration.

The volume (c ml.) of the flask and stopper is determined by weighing it when empty and when filled with mercury. The factor for the calculation of volume from the weight of mercury at the prevailing temperature is taken from one of the published tables. The flasks and manometers to be used in the Warburg apparatus are then calibrated separately in conjunction with A and B. To do this the manometer flask D is first filled with mercury and the stopper A

inserted so that its capillary is filled. The volume of mercury so contained is v ml. Now the manometer volume is determined. The small
flask B is filled with mercury and pressed on to the ground joint of
the manometer which should be lightly greased, as during a determination. This action causes the mercury to rise in the manometer
capillary side-arm until it fills this as far as the T-junction with the
U-tube of the manometer. The excess mercury flows away down the
U-tube. The main limb of the manometer is now filled with mercury
from the top stopcock down to the zero mark to which the manometer
fluid will normally be levelled in use. In this case this is the 150-mm.
centre calibration. The total quantity of mercury is now run into a
tared beaker and weighed, giving the volume (m ml.) of the manometer and flask B. Now the volume (V ml.) of the manometer
capillary to the zero mark and the manometer flask is given by:

$$V = m - c + v \quad (see \text{ Fig. 55})$$

It is convenient to write on the back of each manometer the value
of ($m - c$) expressed in ml. and to keep a record of the values of v
for the various manometer flasks. The volume of any combination of
flask and manometer can then be worked out.

The flask constant K (64)

In the determination $x = h\mathbf{K}$

where $\qquad x = \mu$ litres gas (0°C and 760 mm. pressure)

$\qquad h =$ the observed change in the manometer
$\qquad\qquad$ (open side) reading in mm.

$\qquad \mathbf{K} =$ flask constant

$$\mathbf{K} = \frac{V_g \dfrac{273}{T} + V_f \propto}{P_0}$$

where $\qquad V_g =$ volume in μ litres of the gas phase in the
$\qquad\qquad$ flask including the connecting tubes down
$\qquad\qquad$ to the 150-mm. point on the closed end
$\qquad\qquad$ of the manometer

$\qquad V_f =$ volume in μ litres of the fluid in flask
$\qquad\qquad$ (i.e. total volume $- V_f = V_g$)

$\qquad P_0 =$ 760 mm. mercury expressed in terms of
$\qquad\qquad$ the manometer fluid (i.e.

$$P_0 = 760 \times \frac{13{\cdot}60}{\text{S.G. of manometer fluid}} \Big)$$

T = temperature of bath in absolute degrees (273 + temp. in °C)

$\propto$ = solubility of gas in the liquid in the flask expressed as ml. gas/ml. liquid, when gas is at pressure of 1 atmosphere at the temperature T.

Calculation of K

There is a simple relationship between the constant K for one set of conditions and the constant for the same conditions except for one extra ml. of fluid in the flask. Let this change be ΔK.

Then

$$\Delta K = K' - K$$

$$= \frac{(V_g - 1000)\dfrac{273}{T} + \propto(V_f + 1000)}{P_0} - \frac{V_g\dfrac{273}{T} + \propto V_f}{P_0}$$

where

K$'$ = constant for flask with 1 extra ml.

K = constant for original flask

$$\Delta K = \frac{-1000\dfrac{273}{T} + 1000\propto}{P_0}$$

Thus ΔK is independent of V_g or V_f and is dependent only upon $\propto$ and T. Thus for any temperature ΔK is easily calculated.

For example: Taking the bath temperature as 30°C and the manometer fluid as S.G. 1·033,

$$\Delta K = -0\cdot024$$

Where there is no fluid in the flask, the constant Ke is independent of the gas and depends only on the volume of the flask and the temperature.

$$Ke = \frac{V_g\dfrac{273}{T}}{P_0} \quad \text{and} \quad \frac{\dfrac{273}{T}}{P_0}$$

is a constant dependent on the temperature, say C.

This constant C can be calculated for any temperature. Taking the example above, C = $0\cdot0901 \times 10^{-3}$.

Now, therefore, the flask constant K can be easily calculated for any set of conditions: K = Ke + (ΔK $\times$ ml. in flask)

$$= (V_g \times C) + (\Delta K \times ml.)$$

129

So taking example above, $T = 30°C$, manometer fluid = 1·033, ml. = 2·2 ml. and flask volume (determined as described previously) = 20,121 μ litres.

$$K = (20,121 \times 0·0901 \times 10^{-3}) + (-0·024 \times 2·2) = 1·76$$

Preparation of manometer. After the flasks and manometer have been calibrated, the manometers are charged with Brodie's fluid. This consists of:

> 23 gm. sodium chloride
> 5 gm. sodium choleate
> 500 ml. water with Evans blue or acid fuchsin.

The density of this fluid should be 1·033.
An alternative to Brodie's fluid is:

> 22·84 gm. sodium bromide
> 0·5 gm. stergine
> 0·3 gm. methylene blue
> 500 ml. water.

The manometer should be perfectly clean and free from grease. The fluid can be introduced by piercing the reservoir with a hypodermic syringe and injecting the fluid. This fluid should be changed periodically otherwise evaporation will affect the specific gravity of the fluid.

Preparation of the L-glutamic acid decarboxylase. Clostridium welchii S.R.12 can be used as a source of the decarboxylase. The total crop from 500 ml. medium is centrifuged and washed with 0·45% sodium chloride solution. The crop is then suspended in 25 ml. of 0·45% sodium chloride solution and stored in a refrigerator.

Possibly a more active decarboxylase is prepared from *Escherichia coli*. The organism is first grown on agar slabs and 100 ml. of the medium are inoculated at 30°C for 24 hours. Sixteen litres are made up consisting of:

> 100 gm. sodium chloride
> 100 gm. pepticase
> 10 gm. yeast extract
> 100 gm. dextrose
> 25 gm. dipotassium hydrogen phosphate

made up to 10 litres with distilled water.

The solution should be made up in a serum bottle and sterilised in an autoclave at 12 lb. for 40 minutes. This medium is then inoculated with the sub-culture and incubated at 25°C for 48 hours. The *E. coli* is then harvested in a centrifuge and washed with several volumes of 0·5% sodium chloride solution, after which it is respun and re-washed. The resulting paste is dried over calcium chloride in a vacuum desiccator for some days, then ground to a powder.

Assay of the Decarboxylase

Reagents: Suspension of E. coli. A suspension of the dried decarboxylase is prepared by mixing it with the acetate buffer solution in the ratio 0·02 gm. per 1 ml. of buffer solution.

Buffer solution. 0·2 M acetate buffer pH 4·7. This consists of 160 ml. 0·2 M sodium acetate (27·22 gm. of the trihydrate to 1,000 ml. water) plus 100 ml. 0·2 M acetic acid (12 gm. glacial to 1,000 ml. water).

Standard L-*glutamic acid solution.* This should be prepared from the pure chemical with water and should contain about 0·002 gm. per ml. *Procedure.* Measure 1 ml. of the standard glutamic acid solution into the main compartment of a Warburg flask, followed by 0·2 ml. of the buffer solution. Place 1 ml. of the *E. coli* suspension in the side-arm of the flask. A blank and a thermobar are also prepared. The side-arm plug should be greased with lanoline and ground into position and a visual examination of the joint must be made to ensure no leaks. Grease the manometer joint and put the flask firmly into position with a spring support. Again, the joint should be examined. Place the manometer and flask into position in the water bath and agitate for 15 minutes to stabilise the temperature at 28° to 30°C. Screw up the manometer reservoir until the indicating fluid is almost to the top of the manometer. Close the manometer tap and gradually open the manometer reservoir until the closed side-arm of the manometer reads 150 mm. Allow the manometer to agitate until stable conditions are established and then readjust to the 150-mm. mark carefully and read the height of the open side of the manometer.

With a finger lightly covering the open end of the manometer, and the other hand supporting the manometer tube against the scale, remove the assembly from the bath and tip so that the *E. coli* suspension enters the main compartment of the flask. Replace immediately in the water bath.

Allow to agitate, and after 5 minutes adjust the closed side of the manometer to 150 mm. Repeat every 5 minutes until the readings are constant, which indicates that the evolution of carbon dioxide is complete.

The reaction with *E. coli* as the active enzyme source will be very rapid and is usually complete in 20 minutes.

(Final manometer reading − initial manometer reading)
− (Thermobar + blank) gives the value of *h*.

Due regard must be given to the sign of the thermobar and the blank.

Using the equation $x = h\mathrm{K}$, the volume of carbon dioxide can be obtained (0°C and 760 mm. pressure).

Knowing that 1 molecule of glutamic acid is equivalent to 22·4 litres of carbon dioxide at N.T.P., the assay of the standard glutamic acid solution can be worked out.

Unknown sample determination. Having determined that the de-carboxylase is active and that the conditions used give an accurate value, the way is clear to examine unknown samples for L-glutamic acid content. The procedure is the same as in the assay determination above. The sample under examination should be treated with sodium hydroxide or hydrochloric acid to bring the pH to 4·5–4·9 and should be diluted with distilled water so that 1 ml. contains approximately 0·002 gm.

AMYLOGLUCOSIDASE ENZYME ASSAY

The modern method for the production of dextrose monohydrate is by the use of a specific enzyme to convert the starch into dextrose. Throughout the world there are commercially available a number of amyloglucosidases for this purpose, and some method must be used for the evaluation of their dextrose-producing ability.

The following method (65) is in constant use:

Reagents. Sodium acetate buffer. 1 molar, pH 4·2. Dissolve 41·0 gm. anhydrous sodium acetate (or 68 gm. hydrated) in 375 ml. of distilled water and adjust the pH to 4·2 using glacial acetic acid and a glass electrode pH-meter. Quantitatively transfer to a 500-ml. volumetric flask and bring to the mark with distilled water.

Starch substrate. 4% w/v solution of 'Analar' soluble starch (B.D.H. Ltd.). A slurry of 20 gm. dry starch in distilled water (the starch moisture must be known and the amount calculated to give 20 gm. on a moisture-free basis) is added to 300 ml. vigorously boiling distilled water. Gently boil with constant stirring for 3 minutes. Remove from the heat and quantitatively transfer to a 500-ml. Pyrex volumetric flask and cool to room temperature under running water. To the cooled starch solution add 28·0 ml. acetate buffer, mix well and make up to the mark with water. This solution should be freshly prepared as required.

Enzyme solution. The enzyme solution should be of such a concentration that 1 ml. will mediate hydrolysis of 20% to 30% of the substrate during the incubation period.

Sodium hydroxide. 2N aqueous solution.

132

Phenolphthalein alcohol indicator solution.

All the necessary reagents for the determination of reducing sugar by the method described elsewhere in this chapter.

Procedure. (1) Accurately dispense 50 ml. of the buffered starch substrate into a 100-ml. volumetric flask and heat in a water bath at 60°C for 15 minutes. Prepare a sufficient number of flasks for enzyme digests and for substrate blank controls.

(2) At zero time, rapidly add 1 ml. enzyme solution to the substrate flasks and swirl gently to mix the contents. For the substrate blank add 1 ml. distilled water instead of the enzyme solution.

(3) After each substrate flask has been incubated for exactly 1 hour, remove it from the water bath, rapidly add 4 drops of phenolphthalein indicator and sufficient 2 N sodium hydroxide solution to produce a pale-pink colour. Cool to room temperature under running water.

Bring the volume of the flasks up to the mark with water and determine the dextrose content of a 5-ml. aliquot by the modified Lane and Eynon method described in this chapter. It has been found that the solution after addition of 2 N sodium hydroxide can be held for as long as 24 hours without any significant increase in the sugar content.

From the estimation of reducing sugars the weight of dextrose present can be calculated, and this is then referred back to the weight of the original enzyme. The activity is then expressed as the weight of enzyme which will produce one gram of dextrose under the conditions of the experiment.

ALKALI FLUIDITY OF STARCH

In the manufacture of some of the modified starches, and in particular the acid-modified wheat starches, the scale of modification is based on the so-called alkali fluidity of the material. Generally speaking the lower the viscosity the higher the fluidity, i.e. fluidity can be regarded as inverse viscosity. This determination is very useful in actual production control but as an accurate measurement of viscosity it is open to very serious criticism. Under the conditions of the test it will rarely happen that the starch paste is completely homogeneous, and the effect of the alkaline medium varies from starch to starch depending on the history of the starch. As in so many cases, however, this empirical test has proved and is still proving very useful in the works' control laboratory.

Equipment. 250-ml. beaker.

Fluidity funnel, which is usually made of metal and is

accurately drilled to give a standard rate of flow (Fig. 56).
100 ml. graduated cylinder.
10 ml. pipette.
Water bath, controlled thermostatically.

Reagents. Exactly 1% w/w sodium hydroxide solution is prepared from carbon-dioxide-free caustic. This can be prepared by making a known saturated solution of sodium hydroxide and filtering when cold, since the precipitated sodium carbonate is insoluble in the cold concentrated solution of sodium hydroxide.

Standardisation of funnel. This is done by holding a finger over the bottom of the run-out bore and pouring into the funnel about 110 ml. of distilled water at 75°F. The funnel itself should be at this temperature and should be supported in a suitable stand. (To get the metal funnel at this temperature it should have been immersed for some time in a water bath at this temperature.) The finger is removed and the flow of water allowed to fall into the 100-ml. graduated cylinder. The time taken for 100 ml. of water to flow from the funnel should be between 70 and 75 seconds. This time is used in the determination.

FIG. 56. Fluidity funnel.

Determination. The moisture content of the starch under test must be known and, using this figure, sufficient starch is weighed out to be equivalent to 4·5 gm. dry starch. This is transferred to the beaker and 10 ml. distilled water are added and the mixture stirred to a smooth paste. 90 ml. of the 1% sodium hydroxide solution at 75°F are added and the slurry stirred continuously for exactly 3 minutes. The beaker is then placed in the water bath for 30 minutes at 75°F. The funnel should be kept in the bath for the same time and allowed to drain for several minutes before the 30-minute period for the starch paste is complete. The funnel should not be wiped out, but only drained.

While holding one finger over the funnel drain-bore, the starch paste is poured into the funnel. Some of the paste is allowed to flow through the funnel until the bore is free from air-bubbles, and this paste is returned into the funnel. The graduated cylinder is placed under the funnel and the flow timed for 70–75 seconds (the exact

134

time has been determined in the standardisation experiment). At the end of this time the flow is interrupted by replacing the finger and removing the cylinder. The volume is read off in the cylinder and the number of millilitres indicated is the alkali fluidity number.

FAT IN STARCH

Most starches in common use contain fatty material, and this is the case with wheat starch. The fat is in close association with the starch and is not completely separated by the physical measures employed during the starch manufacture. The fatty content of the starch can be an embarrassment in modification or conversion processes, and a good illustration of this is the hydrolysis of starch into dextrose. After the required digestion period for the enzyme action and when the starch has been converted into a solution of dextrose, a considerable quantity of residue is found floating in the reaction liquor. This contains, among other substances, substantial amounts of fatty acids.

It is obviously desirable to keep the fat content of starch as low as possible and the following method can be used as a control measure.

Apparatus. Soxhlet extraction aappratus. Double paper extraction thimble or Alundum thimble.

Reagents. Petroleum ether, B.P. 40°–60°C.

Benzene-alcohol mixture of equal parts by volume of benzene and ethyl alcohol. Add 2 ml. of 1% phenolphthalein solution.

Standard potassium hydroxide solution 0·05 N.

Procedure. Weigh 10 gm. of starch into the extraction thimble and extract for about 8 hours. Evaporate the solvent on a steam water bath and weigh the extracted fat. When multiplied by 10, this will give the weight of material extracted as a percentage. Now dissolve this extract in the extraction flask with 50 ml. of benzene-alcohol solvent. Titrate with the potassium hydroxide solution to a faint pink end point. A blank should be carried out on 50 ml. of the benzene-alcohol mixture and this must be subtracted from the titre of the sample. The results can be expressed as ml. of 0·05 N potassium hydroxide solution per 100 gm. of starch.

STARCH PASTES

It is often desirable to obtain the pasting performance of a starch in water over the period from the time swelling begins, through the maximum level of consistency and to the level when cooled to a given temperature. The Brabender Viscograph is a machine on which the permanent pasting history of a starch can be obtained. The Viscograph consists of a cylindrical cup containing vertical pins which is surrounded by an electrical heating element. The cup is rotated steadily by a motor and this free movement is not interfered with by the surrounding heater, which transmits heat by radiation only. The starch paste is contained within the cup, and a feeler unit, consisting of a disc to which are attached several rods extending into the paste, is connected to a sensitive balance system and a recording pen. When the cup is rotated, the feeler turns by an amount depending on the viscosity of the material under test, and the change of viscosity is recorded as a curve. The temperature is increased during the automatic heating phase at a rate of 1·5°C per minute by means of a spiral contact thermometer which is slowly rotated over a gear transmission, the motor driving the cup. However, the temperature can be kept constant if desired.

Also immersed in the starch paste is a water-cooling coil, and this is automatically switched on to give a controlled rate of cooling— 1·5°C per minute—when the cooling phase is required. Therefore in this machine the starch paste can be subjected to a period of controlled heating, a period of constant elevated temperature, a period of controlled cooling and, throughout, a constant shear force, owing to the constant cup rotation at 75–80 r.p.m. Several sequences of heating and cooling can be used to trace a curve, but a convenient one is shown below.

Automatic heating to 92°C (95°C is sometimes used) held at this temperature for 10 minutes, automatic cooling to 50°C, and then held at this temperature for 10 minutes. The starch concentration in water is variable and determined by the level of the viscosity in the starch. A starch displaying a very high level of paste viscosity will be examined at a lower concentration than a starch displaying a low level of paste viscosity.

Typical curves are shown in Fig. 57.

The points on the curve of practical significance are:

(1) The peak B.U. (Brabender Unit) value. Any manufacturer using the starch and cooking to a paste will have to cook through this maximum consistency. This will be the point of greatest 'hold-up' power.
(2) The B.U. value at 92°C or 95°C. In relation to the peak, this reflects the ease of cooking completely.
(3) The B.U. value after 10 minutes or longer at 92°C or 95°C. This shows the stability under heat conditions. This is an important

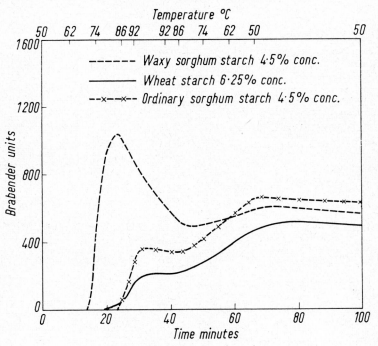

FIG. 57. Pasting history of starches.

consideration to the manufacturer of processed goods containing starch or to the canner of starch-containing foods.

(4) The B.U. value at 50°C, which is a measure of gel or 'set-back' formation on cooling.

(5) The B.U. value after 10 minutes or more at 50°C. This will be a measure of cold paste stability.

The Brookfield Viscometer is a very desirable instrument to have in the laboratory for the examination of the flow properties of starch pastes. The principle of operation of this instrument is very simple. The Viscometer rotates a cylinder or disc in the paste and measures the torque necessary to overcome the viscous resistance to the induced rotation. This is done by driving the immersed metal spindle through a beryllium copper spring, and the amount by which the spring is wound is indicated by the position of a pointer on the Viscometer dial. This degree of lag or wind is proportional to the viscosity of the starch paste for any given speed and type of spindle.

This instrument can measure the rheological properties of the starch paste by using the same spindle at different speeds, and a viscosity/temperature curve can be drawn by using the same spindle and speed at different temperatures. As a check for this last purpose a cooling cycle can be employed.

In the Viscometer a synchronous inductor-type motor and gear transmission are housed above the main case, in which is located the calibrated spring. One end of the spring is attached to a pivot shaft, while the other end is attached directly to the dial. The dial is driven by the gear transmission and this in turn drives the pivot shaft through the calibrated spring. The pointer is attached to the pivot shaft. The pivot shaft is connected to the lower shaft through a bearing arrangement.

To make a reading, a spindle is attached to the lower shaft, taking care not to thrust the spindle out of perfect alignment. The starch paste under examination should be contained in a large beaker of approximately 1,000 ml. capacity. The spindle is now inserted in the paste until the level of the paste is up to the immersion groove cut in the spindle shaft. The Viscometer should be levelled, the clutch

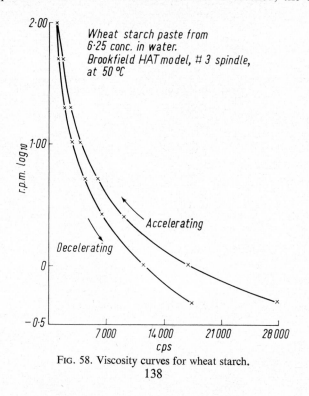

FIG. 58. Viscosity curves for wheat starch.

138

depressed, and the motor turned on. The clutch is released to allow the dial to rotate until the pointer stabilises at a fixed position on the dial. At low speeds it will be possible to observe the position of the pointer, but at high speeds it is necessary to depress the clutch and turn the motor switch off in order to stop the dial with the pointer in view. The viscosity of the starch under test can be obtained in centi-poises by multiplying the dial reading with a constant obtained by consulting the tables supplied with the Viscometer.

In Fig. 58 curves are shown for viscosity against spindle speed $\log_{10}$. It can be seen that there is some decline in the viscosity values under decelerating conditions. This shows the effect of shear energy upon the paste structure.

SEPARATION OF AMINO-ACIDS BY PAPER CHROMATOGRAPHY

Although glutamic acid is by far the most predominant amino-acid present in the wheat gluten hydrolysates, other amino-acids are present in appreciable quantities. This can be demonstrated by the simple separation experiments described below:

Paper disc method (unidimensional). Very little equipment is re-quired for this method: two dishes of the petri type, and filter papers (Whatman No. 1, diameter 9 cm.), being all that is needed. Two variations can be tried: (*a*) the mixture of amino-acids in the hydro-lysate is spotted at the centre of the filter paper and a wick 5 mm. wide is cut from the paper itself (*see* Fig. 59B); (*b*) the amino-acids

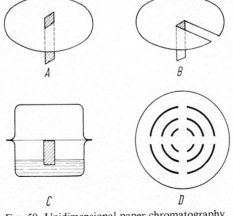

FIG. 59. Unidimensional paper chromatography.

mixture is spotted in four positions round the centre and a slit 5 mm. long is cut through the centre of the paper and a separate wick threaded through (*see* Fig. 59A).

In both cases the solvent is placed in the lower dish and the prepared paper is placed over the top of the dish with the wick hanging down into the solvent. A second dish is carefully inverted over the top (Fig. 59C). Using No. 1 Whatman papers of 9 mm. diameter, approximately four hours are required for the solvent front to reach the working perimeter. The paper is then dried free from the solvent (n-butanol is a suitable choice) and sprayed with ninhydrin to form the characteristic colour compounds, purple and yellow. The type of chromatogram obtained is shown in Fig. 59D, and only amino-acids of widely differing R_f values are usefully separated by this method. From a gluten hydrolysate, the amino-acids are separated into several distinct groups.

Paper-strip method (unidimensional). Under this broad heading, two main types of apparatus are employed: (*a*) ascending development; (*b*) descending development. For the first type of separation the equipment used is shown in Fig. 60A and consists of strips of filter

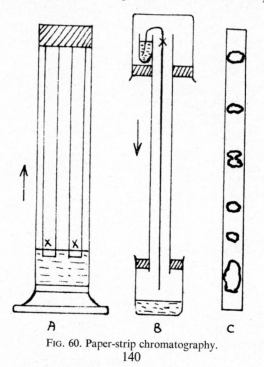

A   B   C

Fig. 60. Paper-strip chromatography.

paper, 1·5 cm. wide, suspended in a two-litre cylinder. Spots of the amino-acid mixture are placed 3 cm. to 4 cm. from the lower ends of the strips which are immersed up to a depth of 1 cm. in the developing solvent (n-butanol is suitable).

For the second method, the apparatus shown in Fig. 60B is used. In this case the amino-acid mixture is spotted on to the highest portion of the paper strip, which is supported with its shorter section dipping into a reservoir of the developing solvent and its longer section down through a glass tube into a tall beaker which contains a small quantity of the solvent, this being in order to saturate the atmosphere. The type of chromatogram obtained in both these cases is the same and is shown in Fig. 60C.

Two-dimensional methods. In the foregoing unidimensional methods using only one solvent, a one-directional spread only is obtained. By using a square paper and treating with two different solvents in directions at right-angles, the separation of the amino-acids is increased.

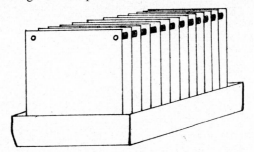

Fig. 61. Apparatus for two-dimensional chromatography.

The groups which have been isolated by the previous methods are now separated into their components.

It has been found that a convenient apparatus (66) for carrying out simple two-dimensional chromatography can be constructed as shown in Fig. 61.

The apparatus is constructed of duralumin and holds up to twelve 20 cm. × 20 cm. squares of filter paper suitably spaced with cylindrical collars. This rests in a trough containing the solvent, and the whole is enclosed in a Perspex container. The amino-acid mixture is spotted on at one corner, and after running the solvent in one direction the papers are dried thoroughly by heating in a well-ventilated oven at 50° to 60°C. High drying-oven temperatures will cause loss by decomposition of the amino-acids. The frame is now replaced in a second solvent, at right-angles to the initial position, and the process repeated. No detachment of the papers is necessary.

There is a wide variety of solvents that can be used, but the following three have been used with success:

(*a*) Phenol

(*b*) Lutidine—collidine—water

(*c*) Butanol—water—acetic acid.

(*a*) A stock solution is prepared by melting 450 gm. A.R. grade phenol (laboratory steam-distilled) in 50 ml. of distilled water. When and as required, portions are withdrawn from the stock solution and shaken with excess of distilled water. After separating the two layers, the aqueous layer is used to condition the container atmosphere, while the phenol layer is used as the developing solvent. It is recommended that a small container of hydrocyanic acid or 8-hydroxyquinoline be present in the Perspex container to retard decomposition on the paper. A trace of ammonia can be used.

(*b*) This solvent is a mixture of 2,6-lutidine—2,4,6-collidine—water. The difficulty in purifying the pyridine compounds can be overcome by steam-distilling a 1 : 1 mixture of lutidine and collidine and using the aqueous layer obtained for container atmosphere-conditioning and the oil layer for elution.

(*c*) 500 ml. n-butanol and 500 ml. of distilled water are shaken together in a separating funnel, whereupon 60 ml. glacial acetic acid are added and the whole shaken again. Both the layers obtained can be used for solvent purposes, and are stored together to reduce the extent of esterification.

The solvent used for the initial elution is phenol and one of the other two solvents is used for the second treatment. Both give good results, with perhaps a preference for the butanol mixture (68).

The chromatograms obtained are shown in Figs. 62, 63 and 64.

To identify the component amino-acids of the finished chromatogram, it is necessary to refer to a standard chromatogram which should be prepared under the same conditions as the test. A whole series of known amino-acids are individually spotted out on to the square filter papers and the R_f values determined for each amino-acid in each dimension. Taking these two R_f values for each amino-acid, its position can be worked out on a two-dimensional chromatogram. This enables the standard chromatogram to be drawn out and from this the relative (not absolute) positions of the various amino-acids can be seen. When a mixture of these known amino-acids is spotted out and developed two-dimensionally, it will be seen that there is some mutual interference in the movement of each amino-acid, and that the actual position on the finished chromatogram has altered. However, the relative positions will not have changed.

For a confirmation of any particular amino-acid, parallel chroma-

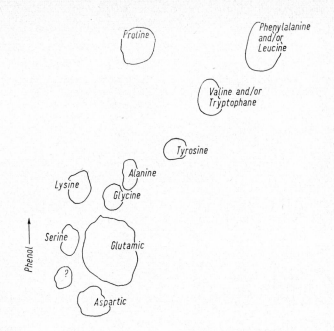

FIG. 62. Butanol—water—acetic acid chromatogram.

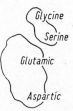

FIG. 63. Lutidine—collidine—water chromatogram (in presence of NH₃).

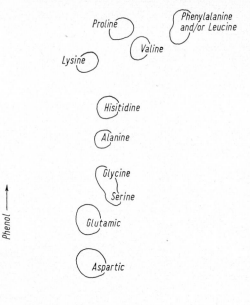

FIG. 64. Lutidine—collidine—water chromatogram (in presence of HCN).

tograms are run but only one is sprayed with ninhydrin. When the positions have appeared as coloured spots, the corresponding area or areas on the other paper can be cut out and extracted, and known chemical confirmation tests applied to the solutions.

This chromatographic procedure for the separation of amino-acids can be developed into a quantitative test. After developing the coloured areas the individual spots can be cut out, extracted, and the optical density of the solutions can be compared with standard colour solutions from known quantities of the amino-acid in question.

DEGREE OF SUBSTITUTION IN STARCH ETHERS (67)

The estimation is based on the reaction of hydriodic acid with the hydroxyethyl ether of starch. The halogen acid splits the ether linkage very effectively, and takes various courses depending upon the reaction conditions. In the cold the reaction is as follows:

$$R—O—CH_2—CH_2·OH + HI \rightarrow R—OH + I·CH_2·CH_2·I + H_2O$$
where R = Starch

144

As the temperature is increased, in the presence of excess hydriodic acid, the starch reacts with another molecule of the acid:

$$R{-}OH + HI \rightarrow RI + H_2O$$

The starch iodide is non-volatile, insoluble and is a tar-like product. The 1,2 di-iodoethane is very unstable and decomposes as follows:

$$I{\cdot}CH_2{\cdot}CH_2{\cdot}I \rightarrow CH_3{\cdot}CH_2{\cdot}I + I_2$$
$$I{\cdot}CH_2{\cdot}CH_2{\cdot}I \rightarrow CH_2{=}CH_2 + I_2$$
$$CH_2{=}CH_2 + HI \rightarrow CH_3{\cdot}CH_2{\cdot}I$$

The two final reaction products are ethyl iodide and ethylene, and the sum of these is equivalent to the hydroxy ethyl ether groups in the sample.

In the determination the decomposition products are fractionally distilled from the reaction materials in the flask. Ethylene (B.P. $-104\,°C$) and ethyl iodide (B.P. $72\,°C$) are readily carried over from the reaction-mixture temperature boiling at $150\,°C$. The hydriodic acid is retain by the reflux column, although some iodine is carried over. A trap of red phosphorus is provided to retain this. A cadmium sulphate trap is sometimes included to retain any hydrogen sulphide which will be formed by traces of sulphur compounds present.

The ethylene and ethyl iodide pass into alcoholic silver nitrate which retains the halide as the silver salt in an insoluble yellow form. The unreacted silver nitrate is then estimated by the Volhard method.

The ethylene passes on and is fixed in a bromine—acetic acid—potassium bromide reagent. The ethylene forms the dibromide compound, one mole of bromine reacting with one mole of ethylene. The remaining bromine is titrated with sodium thiosulphate after adding potassium iodide.

Apparatus. The equipment is made from Pyrex glass and has standard ground glass joints. The reaction flask is 100 ml. capacity, with a B24 joint and a capillary side-arm of 1 mm. inside diameter for the introduction of carbon dioxide gas. A fractionating column of the Vigreux type, 40 cm. in length and 18 mm. inside diameter, fits into the flask and is secured by means of springs. The arm at the top of the column is 10 cm. long and connects to a trap A. The connecting tube to trap B narrows along its length. After this trap B is an absorption column, and finally trap C (*see* Fig. 65).

Reagents: Hydriodic acid. Pure acid of specific gravity $1\cdot70$ with a boiling point of $126°$ to $127\,°C$ is required. Normal-reagent grade can be purified as follows:

A 2-litre, round-bottomed, three-necked flask is fitted with a thermometer pocket, a condenser and a dropping-funnel. 35 gm. of red phosphorus and 500 ml. of water are placed in the flask. The flask is slowly heated in an oil bath and 400 gm. of iodine in 400 ml.

145

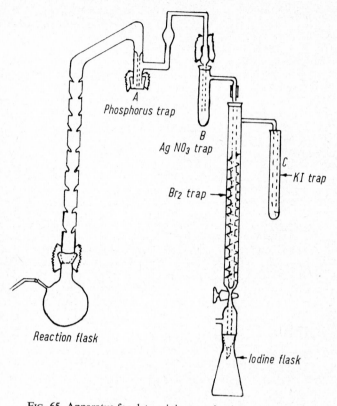

A
Phosphorus trap

B
Ag NO₃ trap

C
← KI trap

Br₂ trap →

Reaction flask

← Iodine flask

FIG. 65. Apparatus for determining starch ether substitution.

of hydriodic acid are slowly added from the dropping-funnel. The mixture is heated to constant boiling for 30 minutes. The supernatant liquid is transferred to an all-glass distillation equipment and fractionally distilled, under carbon dioxide. A heavy reflux is required with a slow rate of distillation. The fraction boiling and distilling at 126° to 127°C is collected separately and redistilled in the same equipment. After the second collection the acid is transferred to a dark bottle and stored under carbon dioxide.

Bromine solutions. 10 gm. of potassium bromide A.R. are added to 600 ml. of glacial acetic acid. To this mixture is added a 2-ml. volume of A.R. bromine. The solution must be stored in a dark bottle. The standardisation of the bromine solution is done with 0·05 N sodium thiosulphate.

Silver nitrate solution. 15 gm. of A.R. silver nitrate are dissolved in 28 ml. of water and added to 422 ml. of 95% ethanol. Several drops of concentrated nitric acid are also added. This solution is also kept in a dark bottle. About 44 ml. of 0·05 N ammonium thiocyanate are required for the titration by the Volhard method.

Ammonium thiocyanate solution. A solution of ammonium thiocyanate at 0·05 N concentration is prepared by weighing out 3·8062 gm. of the salt and dissolving it to 1,000 ml. of solution. This is now standardised in the usual manner against 0·05 N silver nitrate or against pure silver foil dissolved in nitric acid (1 : 1). A 0·05 N silver nitrate solution is prepared by directly dissolving 4·2473 gm. of the salt to 500 ml. of solution. The ammonium thiocyanate is titrated against the silver nitrate using the Volhard method and, as indicator, 4 ml. of ferric ammonium sulphate.

$$NH_4CNS + AgNO_3 \rightarrow AgCNS + NH_4NO_3$$

Excess of the thiocyanate reacts with the indicator to form a brown-red coloured complex. This is the end point.

Ferric ammonium sulphate indicator. A saturated solution of ferric ammonium sulphate is prepared, and concentrated nitric acid is added to remove the brown colour.

Sodium thiosulphate. 12·5 gm. of A.R. sodium thiosulphate are dissolved into a litre of solution, and 2 ml. of 0·1 N caustic soda are added. The solution has to be standardised against a potassium iodate 0·05 N solution, which is prepared by dissolving 1·7835 gm. of the pure chemical into 1 litre of solution. 20 ml. of this standard iodate solution are pipetted into an iodine flask containing 100 ml. of water, followed by 10 ml. of 10% potassium iodide solution and 1 ml. of concentrated hydrochloric acid. This is now titrated with the sodium thiosulphate solution until the iodine colour is very faint. At this point several millilitres of starch indicator solution are added and the titration continued until no blue colour reappears upon standing for 30 seconds. This indicates the complete neutralisation of the free iodine by the thiosulphate, and is the end point.

Starch indicator solution. Water is added to 2 gm. of soluble starch to make a thick paste. This is then added to 200 ml. of boiling water. 2 gm. of potassium iodide are added to the solution.

Potassium iodide solution. 10 gm. of potassium iodide are dissolved into 100 gm. aqueous solution.

Sulphuric acid solution. This is a 10% aqueous solution.

Cadmium sulphate solution. This is a solution of 5 gm. of $3CdSO_4 \cdot 8H_2O$ in 100 ml. of solution.

Procedure. All determinations should be under a ventilation hood. The trap A is prepared by adding several gm. of red phosphorus. A separate trap containing cadmium sulphate solution can be prepared, or this can be included in with the red phosphorus in trap A. The absorption tube is partially filled with 15 ml. of the bromine solution and trap B with 10 ml. of the alcoholic silver nitrate solution. The end trap C holds 10 ml. of 10% potassium iodide solution. The iodine flask is fitted on to the absorption tube and contains 50 ml. of water and 10 ml. of the potassium iodide solution.

Into the reaction flask are placed boiling stones and 40–45 ml. of hydriodic acid. One gm. of the sample is weighed into a gelatin capsule and this is dropped into the flask. The flask is then fixed to the fractionating column and carbon dioxide is passed through the apparatus in a slow stream, 1 to 2 bubbles per second. The flask is heated slowly to 155°C on an oil bath. One and a half hours is usually sufficient for the determination.

In the early part of the reaction the silver nitrate in trap B is quite cloudy, but in time the precipitate settles and the supernatant liquid is quite clear. If the temperature of this trap is below 40°C it should be immersed in hot water to drive out any dissolved olefine.

When the reaction is over, the connection between B and the absorption tube is slowly broken to equalise the pressures. Care should be taken not to lose the contents of the traps. The contents of the absorption tube are allowed to run into the iodine flask via the tap, and the tube and its side-arm into trap C are thoroughly washed with water. The contents of trap C are added to the iodine flask. The next operation is to add the stopper to the flask and allow it to stand for 5 minutes. 5 ml. of 10% sulphuric acid are added and the solution titrated with 0·05 N sodium thiosulphate and 2 ml. of starch indicator. The contents of the silver nitrate trap are rinsed into a flask containing 150 ml. of water. After being heated to boiling and then cooled to room temperature, the solution is titrated with 0·05 N ammonium thiocyanate solution, using 3 ml. of ferric ammonium sulphate as indicator.

A blank determination should be carried out using all the reagents but no sample. Also it is very desirable to check the method and operation against a sample with a known content of ethylene oxide. Carbowax compounds can be used for this. These polyethylene glycols are available in molecular weights ranging from 200 to 20,000. Carbowax is a trade-mark name and belongs to Union Carbide and Carbon Corporation, New York.

Results. The results can be expressed as hydroxy ethyl content or as the ethylene oxide content. Since the reaction of ethylene oxide with starch results in a straight addition of molecular weights to give the molecular weight of the resulting ether, it is convenient to express the results as ethylene oxide content.

$$\frac{\text{(Blank titration ml. NH}_4\text{SCN} - \text{sample titration ml. NH}_4\text{SCN)} \times \text{Normality} \times 4\cdot405}{\text{Wt. of sample in gm.}}$$

$$= \% \text{ ethylene oxide (Trap B)}$$

$$\frac{\text{(Blank titration ml. Na}_2\text{S}_2\text{O}_3 - \text{sample titration ml. Na}_2\text{S}_2\text{O}_3) \times \text{Normality} \times 2\cdot203}{\text{Wt. of sample in gm.}}$$

$$= \% \text{ ethylene oxide (absorption tube)}$$

The total of the two figures gives the amount of ethylene oxide in the starch, combined as hydroxy ethyl ether.

REFERENCES

(1) W. Sech & W. Kempf (1958). *Die Stärke*, **10**, 6–11.
(2) W. M. Honsch (1958). *Ibid.*, **10**, 323–5.
(3) W. M. Honsch (1953). *Ibid.*, **5**, 81–2.
(4) C. O. Reiser (1954). *J. Agric. Food Chem.*, **2**, 70–5.
(5) R. A. Anderson *et al.* (1958). *Cereal Chemistry*, **35**, 449–57.
(6) R. A. Anderson & E. L. Griffin (1962). *Die Stärke*, **14**, 210.
(7) R. J. Dimler *et al.* (1944). *Cereal Chemistry*, **21**, 430.
(8) J. R. Crozier (Jan. 1959). *Canadian Food Industry*.
(9) J. W. Knight & E. G. Woodward (1958). Unpublished data.
(10) D. B. Montgomery & J. G. Moore (1959). U.S. Patent 2,891,045.
(11) W. M. Miley *et al.* (1957). U.S. Patent 2,797,212.
(12) W. B. McConnell (1955). *Can. J. Technol.*, **33**, 256–64.
(13) V. F. Pfeifer *et al.* (1958). *Cereal Chemistry*, **35**, 458.
(14) G. A. Adams (1952). *Ibid.*, **29**, 312.
(15) J. W. Knight & E. G. Woodward (1954). Unpublished data.
(16) J. W. Evans (1957). U.S. Patent 2,806,026.
(17) J. A. Korth (1959). U.S. Patent 2,884,346.
(18) W. Drench & C. L. Mehltretter (1953). U.S. Patent 2,648,629.
(19) C. L. Mehltretter (1955). U.S. Patent 2,713,553.
(20) J. W. Sloan *et al.* (1956). *Ind. Eng. Chem.*, **48**, 1165.
(21) Miles Chemical Company, U.S.A. Unpublished work.
(22) V. C. Barry & P. W. D. Mitchell (1954). *J.C.S.*, 3631; (1953), 4020.
(23) L. Mester (1955). *J.A.C.S.*, **77**, 5452.
(24) C. L. Mehltretter *et al.* (1959). U.S. Patent 2,880,236.
(25) V. C. Barry & P. W. D. Mitchell (1953). *J.C.S.*, 3610.
(26) V. C. Barry *et al.* (1953). *Ibid.*, 3692.
(27) R. L. Mellies *et al.* (1958). *Ind. Eng. Chem.*, **50**, 1311.
(28) B. T. Hofreiter *et al.* (1957). *J.A.C.S.*, **79**, 6457.
(29) J. W. Sloan & I. A. Wolff (1957). U.S. Patent 2,796,447.
(30) J. W. Sloan *et al.* (1957). U.S. Patent 2,783,283.
(31) I. J. Goldstein & F. Smith (1958). *Chem. & Ind.*, Jan. 11th, 40.
(32) R. E. C. Fredrickson (1958). U.S. Patent 2,845,368.
(33) L. L. Phillips & M. L. Caldwell (1951). *J.A.C.S.*, **73**, 3559, 3563.
(34) R. W. Kerr *et al.* (1951). *Ibid.*, **73**, 3916.
(35) J. H. Pazur & T. Ando (1959, 1960). *J. Biol. Chem.*, **234**, 1966; **235**, 297.
(36) T. J. Schoch (1945). *Advances in Carbohydrate Chemistry*, **1**, 247.
(37) Co-operative Verkoop. British Patents 722,586 (1955); 779,261 and 779,262 (1957).
(38) H. Neukom (1958). U.S. Patent 2,865,762.
      L. W. Ferrara (1958). U.S. Patent 2,865,763.
      H. Neukom (1958). U.S. Patent 2,824,870.

REFERENCES

H. Neukom (1959). U.S. Patent 2,884,412.

R. Kodras (1961). U.S. Patent 2,971,954.

J. W. Frieders (1961). U.S. Patent 2,974,049.

H. Neukom (1961). U.S. Patent 2,977,236.

F. A. Hoglan & J. W. Sietsema (1961). U.S. Patent 2,988,453.

J. W. Sietsema & W. C. Trotter (1961). U.S. Patent 2,993,041.

(39) Beccari (1745). *De Bononiensi Scientiarum et Artium Instituto Atque Academia.* **2**, 122–127.

(40) T. B. Osborne (1907). *Proteins of the Wheat Kernel.* Carnegie Inst., Washington, Public. **84**.

(41) J. H. Woychik *et al.* (1961). *J. Arch. Biochem. Biophys.*, **94**, 477.

(42) J. C. Grosskreutz (1961). *Cereal Chemistry*, **38**, 336.

(43) J. W. Pence *et al.* (1953). *Ibid.*, **30**, 115.

(44) K. Bonni & J. W. Knight (1960). Unpublished data.

(45) J. W. Knight *et al.* (1960). Unpublished data.

(46) W. Fong & H. P. Lundgren (1953). *Textile Research J.*, **76**, 9.

(47) E. S. Sagi (1954). *Trans. Am. Assoc. Cereal Chemists*, **12**, 56.

(48) H. C. Reitz *et al.* (1944). *Ind. Eng. Chem.*, **36**, 1149.

(49) S. Coppick & A. J. Hall (1947). *Flameproofing Textile Fabrics*, 179–190, A.C.S. Monograph 104. Reinhold Publ. Corp.

(50) A. Mohammad *et al.* (1954). *Agric. Food. Chem.*, **2**, 136.

(51) J. W. Pence *et al.* (1950). *Cereal Chemistry*, **27**, 335.

(52) H. Ritthausen (1866). *J. prakt. Chem.*, **99**, 454.

(53) L. Wolff (1890). *Ann. Chem.*, **260**, 79.

(54) F. T. Zimmerman *et al.* (1947). *Psychosomat. Med.*, **9**, 175.

(55) J. W. Knight & E. G. Woodward (1953). Unpublished data.

(56) V. Prey & L. Maier (1960). *Die Stärke*, **12**, 52–58.

(57) J. W. Knight & E. G. Woodward (1953). Unpublished data.

(58) E. J. Cohn & J. T. Edsall (1943). *Protein, Amino-acids and Peptides.* Reinhold, U.S.A.

(59) G. K. Adkins (1957). Unpublished data.

(60) J. R. Fraser *et al.* (1956). *J. Sci. Food Agric.*, **7**, 577.

(61) E. G. Woodward (1961). Unpublished data.

(62) V. Prey & L. Maier (1960). *Die Stärke*, **12**, 52.

(63) F. Dickens (1951). *Biochem J.*, **48**, 385.

(64) W. W. Umbreit *et al.* (1959). *Manometric Techniques.* Burgess Publishing Co., U.S.A.

(65) Miles Chemical Company, U.S.A. Unpublished work.

(66) S. P. Datta *et al.* (1950). *Biochem J.*, **46**, XLII. *Science*, **112**.

(67) H. J. Lortz (1956). *Ann. Chem.*, **28**, 892–95.

(68) J. W. Knight & E. G. Woodward (1954). Unpublished data.

INDEX